C000226608

Beginner's G

Radio

Gordon J. King G4VFV

TEng (CEI), AMIERE, FSERT, FISTC

Heinemann : London

William Heinemann Ltd
10 Upper Grosvenor Street, London W1X 9PA

LONDON   MELBOURNE   JOHANNESBURG   AUCKLAND

First published by George Newnes Ltd 1955
Fifth edition 1962
Sixth edition (third impression) 1968
Seventh edition by Newnes-Butterworths 1970
Eighth edition by Newnes Technical Books 1977
Ninth edition 1984
First published by William Heinemann Ltd 1987

British Library Cataloguing in Publication Data
King, Gordon J.
  Beginner's guide to radio. — 9th ed.
  1. Radio — Apparatus and supplies
  I. Title
  621.3841   TK6560

  ISBN 0 434 91073 2

Photoset by Butterworths Litho Preparation Department
Printed in England by Thetford Press Limited, Thetford, Norfolk.

Preface

Since this is a book for beginners in radio it must necessarily assume that its readers will not be very well versed in the principles of the technology. Readers of the editions that have gone before will probably have by now graduated to higher levels of text, but there will always be new generations of beginners, and this book is dedicated to them.

The plan has been to start at square one, and to progress to the present art of high-quality radio reception, so that the book can be regarded as complete within itself. It is not meant to constitute a textbook, but explains radio technology (from the electron to the sound that emanates from the loudspeaker) with the least mathematics and in a basically non-technical, easily readable style.

Although the thermionic valve is no longer a major feature in contemporary radio receivers (though it is by no means a 'dead duck'), references are still, deliberately, made to it because it represents an important radio principle. Nevertheless, the transistor, integrated circuit and other solid-state devices are the primary runners, in spite of the valve being given the first place in Chapter 7. It must also be appreciated that this is a book on *radio*, not electronics generally, for which there is a separate *Beginner's Guide*.

A great deal of attention has not been given to radio circuits. This, again, is deliberate, since readers sufficiently advanced fully to appreciate circuits would need first to have explored a more basic text such as this one. For circuit description and matters of circuit design and servicing there are hosts of more specialised books.

While revising for the ninth edition I have taken the opportunity to include a new chapter on Citizen's Band (CB) radio and information on CB aerials. I have also updated some of the original text for readers intending to use the book as an aid to their studies for the Radio Amateur Examination (RAE).

Although the earlier editions were not primarily intended for this purpose, I have been encouraged by the number of enthusiasts who have nevertheless found this book helpful for graduating from CB to amateur radio. It is surprising just how many of our fraternity are now keen to acquire a Class B amateur-radio transmitting licence, despite its HF bands and CW (morse) restrictions, since having had their interest whetted by their experiences of CB radio.

In conclusion, I would like to thank the many thousands of readers of my previous editions, particularly those – and reviewers – who have submitted positive suggestions for this new edition, some of which have been included.

G.J.K.

Contents

1

Electricity and magnetism

As radio is one manifestation of electricity and magnetism working hand-in-hand, we must start with a brief investigation into the principles of electricity and magnetism.

Electricity stems from the controlled movement of electrons, which means that we can regard electrons as potential or 'passive' electricity, and electrons in orderly movement as 'active' electricity. Electrons are not merely the producers of electricity; they are, in fact, component parts of all and every piece of matter in existence.

If it were possible to continue cutting up, say, a piece of copper into smaller and smaller pieces, we would ultimately reach a final stage of division where the resulting, incredibly small particle would be a copper *atom*. Because copper is an *element*, all its atoms of the same type. A substance composed of two or more kinds of atoms is a *compound*. Atoms of the same or different kind held together by molecular force constitute a combination known as a *molecule*. A well known example is water, which is composed of molecules each composed of two atoms of hydrogen and one of oxygen.

Each atom of every kind of matter consists of two primary components – the *electron* and the *proton*. Over the years various other sub-atomic particles have been discovered, including the meson and neutron, but while they are important in the study of nuclear physics, they hold little or no importance in the basic study of radio.

The electrons and protons style each atom like a

diminutive solar system, the central *nucleus* consisting of the protons, etc., while the electrons in orbit round this can be likened to the planets. The nucleus is a very dense part and is made up of one or more protons (and possible other sub-atomic particles) in very close proximity.

By convention, an electron carries a charge of negative electricity and a proton a charge of positive electricity. In any uncharged atom, the negative and positive charges are equal, the atom then being electrically neutral.

A small particle of copper the size of a pinhead contains about 10^{18} atoms (that is, 1 followed by 18 noughts!). Such small size is difficult to appreciate; but electrons do have mass (9×10^{-28} gram). A proton is about 1800 times more massive than an electron (1.63×10^{-24} gram), and in relative scale a whole 'universe' of space exists between the nucleus and the electrons of an atom.

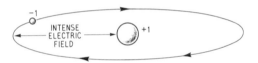

Figure 1.1. The least complex atom is hydrogen, with one proton and one electron

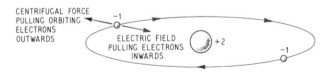

Figure 1.2. An atom of helium has a nucleus of two protons, and there are two charge-balancing orbiting electrons. The electrons fail to leave the realm of the atom in spite of the resulting centrifugal force because they are attracted to the nucleus; hence the development of an orbit, rather like the planets round the sun

Hydrogen is the least complicated atom of all substances, with its solitary electron orbiting its nucleus carrying the charge of one proton, as shown in Figure 1.1. Hydrogen is thus a very light gas of atomic number 1. Helium is another light gas whose atom consists of two electrons and a balancing charge of two protons, as shown in Figure 1.2; its atomic number is 2.

The ion

A complicated atom could have more than ninety orbiting electrons and balancing proton charges, revealed by its atomic number. Thorium, for example, has an atomic number of 90, plutonium 94. Although intrinsically neutral, an atom can become charged negatively by acquiring extra electrons from an adjacent atom, or positively by losing electrons, the result being a negative or positive *ion*.

Complicated atoms also have multiple electron paths. Electrons orbiting along a path close to the nucleus are more tightly bound than those orbiting outer paths. Electrons on an outer path can sometimes move easily to the outer path of an adjacent atom.

Free electrons

An atom of carbon (atomic number 6) has six electrons orbiting a nucleus of six proton charges along two paths

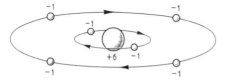

Figure 1.3. An atom of carbon (atomic number 6) has a nucleus of six protons balanced by six orbiting electrons along two paths. Carbon is a good conductor of electricity

(Figure 1.3). Electrons in outer orbit are sometimes called *free electrons*, indicating that they are relatively free to move randomly or as directed by an electric field from atom to atom. These are the electrons responsible for electricity – in contemporary technology called *negative current carriers*.

Conductors and insulators

Conductors of electricity consist of materials whose atoms are endowed with free electrons. Materials whose atoms are of the type where the electrons are bound to the nucleus are called insulators. A conductor offers a free passage to electricity, while an insulator impedes the flow. With a conducting material it requires a relatively small electric charge to transfer the free electrons from atom to atom, while with an insulating material a very high charge is required to shift the tightly bound electrons from their nuclei.

Carbon with its electrons in outer orbit is a good conductor. Copper (atomic number 29) is another example – in fact, one of the best conductors, hence its use for electric cables and radio circuits. The reader will be aware of the conductivity of metals, and will know of many more conductors.

Among the insulators we have glass, plastic materials, ebonite (used extensively in the early days of radio), paraffin wax, ceramics, etc. Air, too, is an insulator; but all insulators, including air, will eventually permit the flow of electricity when the charge is sufficiently high. That is why special insulators with a large surface area are required to support overhead mains cables and very high voltage cables.

As there cannot be a *perfect* insulator, neither can there be a *perfect* conductor under normal conditions. There remains always some resistance (albeit small with the best of conductors) to the movement of the free or mobile electrons. However, it is noteworthy in passing that when a conductor is taken down to the temperatures of liquid gases a condition of *super-conductivity* exists. The free electrons are made even more mobile, and once electric conduction is started the supply source can be removed and the current continues to flow. Superconductivity also makes it possible to develop extremely powerful electric magnets.

Semiconductors

When a very good insulator in the form of a crystalline base has 'impurities' added to it, in the form of atoms with mobile electrons, the insulator becomes conductive under certain conditions. The controlled addition of atomic impurities, in fact, produces the so-called *semiconductor*, which is used in diodes, rectifiers, transistors, integrated circuits, etc. (see Chapters 7 and 8).

Electricity

Electricity, then, is the controlled movement of electrons in a material. Imagine a length of copper wire whose atoms have an abundance of free or mobile electrons. These are normally dodging randomly from atom to atom. This does not produce useful electricity, however. In fact, the random movement of electrons is an embarrassment to the radio engineer. A sensitive radio receiver not tuned to a station but adjusted to full gain will produce from a connected loudspeaker a loud hiss resulting from the random move-ment of electrons in the various conductors and components at the front of the receiver circuit.

Electricity used for heating, lighting, traction, etc. consti-tutes an orderly movement of mobile electrons from atom to atom within the conductor. This occurs when the conductor is connected, say, across the terminals of a battery. One end of the conductor is then positive and the other end negative.

A basic law of electricity (and magnetism) is that like charges (and poles) repel and unlike ones attract. Thus the positive charge at one end of the conductor tends to attract the electrons from that end, while the negative charge at the other end tends to force the electrons into the conductor. Although not a very scientific explanation, it gives a mental picture of what happens. The electric charge across the conductor 'pressurises' the electrons, so to speak, rather like the pressure in a water pipe. Unlike water, however, the electrons cannot normally fall out of the conductor. There must be an external circuit of some kind to provide continuity. The electric source, in fact, can be regarded as an 'electron pump'.

The source can be a battery or generator – or something that creates an electric charge across its terminals. The source has an abundance of mobile electrons, and just as a water pump must be primed before it will operate, so must the source contain sufficient mobile electrons. Thus the flow of electrons is from the source, through the conductor and then back to the source. The flow ceases when the electric pressure is cut off – for example, when the battery runs down or the generator ceases to turn.

Current flow

In this way a continuous movement of electrons is sustained from the negative to the positive charge, which is the direction of *electron flow*.

Years ago there was some confusion about the direction of the flow of electricity, and before much was known about the electron composition of the atom the flow of electricity was considered to be from positive to negative. Text books still sometimes refer to this direction of flow, calling it the *conventional* direction of flow. However, all through this book the direction of flow is considered as the electron flow – from negative to positive

The flow of electrons constitutes an electric current. The greater the rate of flow, the greater the current. The flow is measured relative to the time of one second. However, because of the incredibly small size of an electron it is impracticable to measure the current in terms of the number of electrons passing a given point in the circuit in one second. Instead, a whole lot of electrons is measured, and the unit adopted is the *coulomb* (C). The charge of an electron is 1.6×10^{-19} C, which, in terms of the coulomb, corresponds to the passage of 6.3×10^{18} electron charges per second. The actual rate of flow of current (I) is measured in *amperes* (A), such that 1 A is equal to the passage of 1 coulomb in 1 second. The charge of electricity in coulombs is symbolised by the upper-case letter Q. Thus $Q = It$ or $I = Q/t$, where t is the time in seconds.

In radio circuits the current is often only a few thousandths of an ampere, and the terms milliampere (10^{-3} A) and microampere (10^{-6} A) are used to express such small currents. These are abbreviated respectively to mA and μA. In electric power plants and large industrial projects the current flowing is very much greater, sometimes as high as kiloamperes (kA = 10^3 A) or even megaamperes (MA = 10^6 A).

Cells and batteries

The flow of current depends on the 'electron pressure' and the ease at which the electrons can flow through the circuit. There are various ways of developing electron or *electric pressure*. A common one is chemically by means of an electric cell or battery (a battery is a number of cells connected together – i.e. a *battery* of cells).

There is a wide range of cells: those that need no charging, called *primary cells*, such as used in torches, transistor radios, etc.; and those that require charging before they provide electric pressure, called *secondary cells* or sometimes accumulators, such as used in motor cars.

The simplest primary cell comprises electrodes of copper (positive) and zinc (negative) immersed in sulphuric acid. Current flows when a conductor is connected between the electrodes. The current acts in the acid electrolyte in such a manner as to decompose the acid, one effect being the production of hydrogen gas round the copper electrode. This tends to oppose the cell's electric pressure capabilities, thereby swiftly causing a fall in current flow.

Practical cells avoid this by the use of a *depolariser*.

The most widely used primary cell is based on the Leclanché principle. The electrodes are zinc (negative) and carbon (positive) and the electrolyte is ammonium chloride (NH_4Cl). When the circuit is completed and current flows, zinc chloride ($ZnCl$) is formed, and it is this action that releases electricity by producing a surplus of electrons on one electrode and a deficiency on the other. What happens is that NH_4 positive ions flow to the carbon. This is packed with a mixture of manganese dioxide (MnO_2) and carbon, which neutralise the hydrogen gas and thus serve as the depolariser. The effect is that the NH_4 ions are divided into ammonia gas (NH_3) and hydrogen (H), oxidation then occurring as the

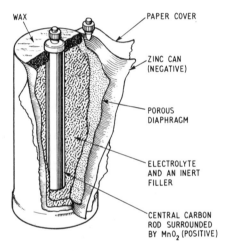

WAX   PAPER COVER

ZINC CAN
(NEGATIVE)

POROUS
DIAPHRAGM

ELECTROLYTE
AND AN INERT
FILLER

CENTRAL CARBON
ROD SURROUNDED
BY MnO_2 (POSITIVE)

Figure 1.4. The composition of a dry primary cell that produces about 1.5 V. A number of such cells constitute a battery of the type used in torches, radios, etc.

result of the MnO_2 to produce water. The depolarisation is able to combat the hydrogen, provided that the current flow is intermittent and not too large.

Early Leclanché cells used liquid electrolyte. The modern versions use a paste electrolyte, hence the term *dry cell.*

Figure 1.4 gives an impression of the inside of a dry primary cell.

A well known secondary cell is the lead–acid storage cell or accumulator, whose electrodes are lead based and electrolyte sulphuric acid. The anode electrode is lead peroxide, which reacts with the sulphuric acid to produce a positive charge. The cathode electrode is metallic lead, which reacts with the acid to produce a negative charge. Sulphate ions and the lead at both electrodes combine to produce a poorly soluble lead sulphate, and the action can be described chemically as below:

$$\underset{(+)}{PbO_2} + 2H_2SO_4 + \underset{(-)}{Pb} \overset{charged}{=} \underset{(+)}{PbSO_4} + 2H_2O + \underset{(-)}{PbSO_4} \quad \text{discharged}$$

The charged condition is achieved by passing a current through the cell. It will be seen that in the charged condition the acid is strong ($2H_2SO_4$) and in the discharged condition weak ($2H_2O$). Also, in the charged condition the positive electrode (PbO_2) is brown and the negative electrode (Pb) grey. In the discharged condition both electrodes revert to sulphate ($PbSO_4$). The state of the cell can thus be determined by measuring the specific gravity of the acid and noting the colour of the electrodes.

There are hosts of other primary and secondary cells, including primary cells of alkali–mercuric oxide, alkali–manganese dioxide, magnesium–manganese dioxide, zinc–air, so-called solid-state and silver–zinc; and secondary cells of sealed nickel–cadmium, silver–zinc as well as the lead–acid species.

New cells are being developed; an interesting one is the fuel cell, which provides the direct conversion of fuel into electrical energy by the use of hydrogen as the fuel and oxygen as the electrode. The hydrogen and oxygen reactants are continuously fed into the cell from external storage, so that electric energy is available whenever required – rather like the mechanical energy available from the internal combustion engine when fed with petrol.

Electromotive force and potential difference

The electric pressure produced by a cell, battery or any other source is measured in terms of voltage by a voltmeter, while the current flowing through the circuit is measured with an ammeter (milliammeter or microammeter, depending on the magnitude of current). Figure 1.5 shows a battery (three cells

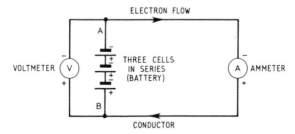

Figure 1.5. Simple circuit with series ammeter to measure current and parallel voltmeter to measure volts. In reality, the battery has an internal resistance (which increases as the battery runs down), so the voltmeter is reading potential difference – see text

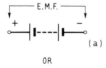

Figure 1.6. Series-connected cells, alternative symbols. The e.m.f. of the battery is equal to the sum of the e.m.f.s of the cells

connected in series) wired in a circuit with an ammeter to measure the current and in parallel with a voltmeter to measure the electric pressure or potential difference across the battery terminals when it is delivering current.

Figure 1.6 shows alternative symbols for series-connected cells, and Figure 1.7 the symbol for four cells connected in parallel. They are both representative of batteries.

The voltage between any two points in an *active* circuit, such as that in Figure 1.5 between points A and B, when the circuit is passing current, is known as the potential difference (p.d.), while the *open-circuit* voltage is called the electro-motive force (e.m.f.). The e.m.f. can be described as that quality which causes a movement of electrons in a circuit. The term is applicable to all sources – chemical, electro-mechanical, thermal, etc. In other words, e.m.f. is the latent force in the source producing the electric pressure.

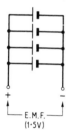

Figure 1.7. Cells connected in parallel. The battery e.m.f. in this case is equal to the cell e.m.f., assuming cells of exactly the same voltage

The common dry cell has an e.m.f. of about 1.5 V, so the four in series in Figure 1.6(b) constitute a battery of about 6 V. The four in parallel in Figure 1.7 result still in a total of 1.5 V, but here the battery has a greater power capacity than that in Figure 1.6. The ordinary lead – acid battery or accumulator produces about 2 V e.m.f. for each of its cells when fully charged, which is why a 12 V car battery contains six cells connected in series.

Ohm's law

All materials at normal temperature impede the movement of electrons, insulators more than conductors. This opposition to current flow is called *resistance* (R), measured in ohms (Ω). The current (I) flowing in a circuit therefore depends not only on the voltage (V) but also on the resistance. One volt drives one ampere through one ohm. This is the basic law

11

expounded by Dr Ohm many years ago. It is best expressed in the following way:

$$V = I \times R, \quad I = V/R \quad \text{or} \quad R = V/I$$

All cells have an internal resistance, which limits the amount of current that can be delivered. When cells are connected in parallel the total resistance is less than the resistance of one cell, which is why cells so connected result in a battery or enhanced power capacity, even though the e.m.f. remains unchanged (see also Chapter 4).

Figure 1.8 shows a battery in a series circuit containing a resistor (see Chapter 4). Let us suppose that the resistor has a value of 100 ohms, the battery an e.m.f. of 9 V and an internal resistance (given by R_i in the circuit) that is very small compared with R_e. In this case the current would be almost equal to 9/100, which works out to 0.09 A or 90 mA. Now let us

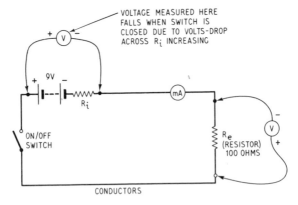

Figure 1.8. A series circuit showing the internal resistance of the battery as R_i and the load resistor as R_e. When the switch is open the voltmeter across the battery indicates virtually the e.m.f. of the battery. With the switch closed, current flows through R_i and R_e, the voltmeter across the battery shows a fall in voltage (depending on the state of the battery) owing to the volts drop across R_i, while the other voltmeter indicates the p.d. across R_e

suppose that the battery is reaching the end of its life, indicated by a rise in R_i to 20 ohms. The circuit would then contain a total series resistance of $100 + 20 = 120$ ohms, which reduces the current to 9/120, i.e. 0.075 A or 75 mA.

In the former case a voltmeter connected across R_e would measure virtually 9 V (assuming negligible circuit resistance), which is the source e.m.f., while in the latter case the voltage would be $0.075 \times 100 = 7.5$ V. This implies a drop of 1.5 V across the internal resistance of the battery. Thus with the switch open a high-resistance voltmeter would read the 9 V e.m.f. of the battery, while with the switch closed the reading would be the p.d. across R_e, again revealing the distinction between e.m.f. and p.d.

This little example also shows the error of checking a battery with a *high-resistance* voltmeter with the battery 'off load'. Even when the battery is nearing exhaustion the voltage would be relatively high under the 'off load' condition because no current (or very little via the voltmeter) is flowing through the internal resistance.

The conductors of the circuit would possess some resistance, albeit small, as also would the series-connected ammeter; but in practical radio work such small values of R do not worry us all that much. In Figure 1.5 a heavy current would flow, limited by the capacity of the battery, its internal resistance and the resistance of the ammeter and conductors. This would subject the battery to a virtual *short-circuit*.

Figure 1.8 also shows the symbols for resistance (or a resistor, which is a component) and a simple single-pole, single-throw on/off switch, which is another component. Such symbols are found extensively in radio circuits.

Power

When current flows through resistance, heat is produced owing to the dissipation of electric power. Even cables of low resistance can warm up when the current flow is substantial. This is why heavy-duty cables of very low resistance are used in power circuits, i.e. on electric fires, cookers, large motors, etc. The heat is the electrical analogue of the heat produced mechanically by friction.

Electric power has the watt (W) as its unit, and is the product of V and I. We have already learned that $V = IR$ and $I = V/R$. Thus power in watts is $W = VI$ (notice that the 'times' or product symbol is usually dropped from these expressions). Bringing in the above simple Ohm's Law expressions, we also find that W is equal to both IRI, which is I^2R, and VV/R, which is V^2/R. To find the power, therefore, we have the choice of three simple expressions, VI, I^2R and V^2/R, and select whichever is most convenient.

In the Internatinal System of Units (SI) the unit of energy is the joule (equal to 10^7 ergs), and 1 W is equal to 1 J/s, where J stands for joule and s for second.

It is often essential to know just how much electric power (or energy) is likely to be dissipated in a circuit or resistor, for overheating could well incite incorrect operation or even failure. In a power circuit, for example, we may have a resistor of, say, 10 ohms connected into a circuit such that, say, 50 V p.d. is developed across the resistor. In this example, the power dissipated by the resistor would be $50^2/10$, i.e. 250 W. The resistor would thus get very hot. It would need to be a wire-wound component designed to withstand high temperature.

Conversely, in the low-power circuits of a radio receiver the current flowing through a 10 000-ohm resistor may be only, say, 5 mA (0.005 A), in which case the power dissipated by the resistor would be a mere $0.005^2 \times 10\,000$, i.e. 0.25 W. Here, then, a relatively small, low-power resistor would be suitable.

Alternating current and direct current

The author recalls during his college days a ditty popular with the students as a memory aid, which went something like 'a.c. volts and d.c. volts and little ohms and amperes, a little inductance too, wouldn't Q...'. This was chanted to the tune of 'Mares eat oats and does eat oats and little lambs eat ivy...'

(which must reveal the author's great age!). We know something about volts, amperes and ohms now, and later should be more familiar with inductance and Q, too.

Now, though, is the time to define a.c. and d.c. The current stemming from a steady flow of electrons *in one direction only* is called *direct current* (d.c. for short). This is the sort of current produced by a cell or battery, though d.c. can also be produced in other ways.

When the current through a circuit changes in direction, either cyclically or as controlled by the source e.m.f., then it is called *alternating current* (a.c. for short). Possibly the best known a.c. is that fed into our homes from the mains supply, which changes direction in a regular sinusoidal manner.

A.C. is also the sort of current associated with radio signals and with the signals from microphones to amplifiers, from radio receivers to loudspeakers, and from gramophone pickups, tape heads, etc. When the current carries sound or audio information, it does not alternate cyclically or always sinusoidally; but instead alternates in accordance with the original sound pressure waves.

The electrons thus flow first in one direction, rising from zero to a maximum value and then falling to zero again, and then in the opposite direction, again rising from zero and then falling to zero again, and so on, changing direction each time.

D.C. can be represented by the straight line shown at (a) in Figure 1.9, while one representation of a.c. is by the curve shown at (b). The curve at (b), in fact, clearly illustrates the positive and negative alternations that must occur at the source to cause the electrons correspondingly to change their direction of flow. The direction reverses for each half-cycle, which implies that a complete waveform is composed of two half-cycles, one positive and the other negative. The current starts from the zero datum line, rises to a maximum and then falls to zero, so completing the positive half-cycle. Exactly the same happens in the opposite direction for completion of the negative half-cycle. The time, taken for a complete cycle to develop (from A to B in the diagram) is a measure of the *frequency* of the a.c. British mains supplies, for example, run at 50 complete waves per second, nowadays called 50 hertz (Hz) – formerly 50 cycles per second (c/s). This means that one complete cycle takes one-fifieth of a second, which is 0.02 s or 20 milliseconds (ms). The SI unit of frequency is always the hertz.

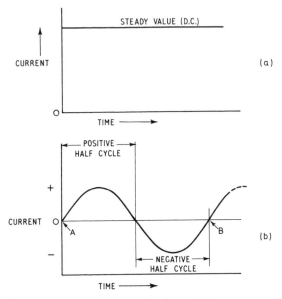

Figure 1.9. Representation of (a) d.c. and (b) a.c.

A.C. waves range from very low frequency (sound waves for instance) to the highest radio frequency, in the order of 10^9 Hz. The abbreviations k, M and G, standing respectively for 'kilo' (=10^3 Hz), 'Mega' (=10^6 Hz) and 'Giga' (=10^9 Hz), are extensively adopted in the literature. Thus we get Hz, kHz, MHz and GHz.

Sine wave

The waveform at (b) in Figure 1.9 is called a sine wave. Figure 1.10(a) shows the same kind of wave displayed on the screen

16

of an oscilloscope (an instrument that employs a cathode-ray tube for displaying waveforms). The term sine wave derives from a geometric function. Consider pointer OX in the circle at the left-hand side of Figure 1.11 to be rotating anticlockwise on its pivot O. The pointer starts at point A on the circle, corresponding to 0 degrees (or 360 degrees after it has been round a turn), and finishes at point A at the conclusion of a complete sine wave.

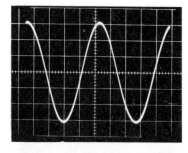

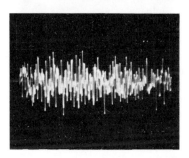

Figure 1.10. (a) Sine wave displayed on the screen of an oscilloscope. Here each horizontal division corresponds to a time period of 0.2 ms (200 μs), so a complete cycle of the wave occupies a time period of about 5 × 0.2 ms, i.e. 1 ms, equal to a frequency of 1/0.001, i.e. 1000 Hz (1 kHz). (b) Waveform of music signal, showing how this differs from the sine wave at (a)

Clearly, as the angle of pointer rotation increases, so also does the length of the broken line XY. The length is zero at point A and maximum at point C, zero again at point E and maximum again at point G. The length of the broken line corresponds to the *amplitude* of the wave from its zero datum line at any instant. It thus becomes possible to construct a sine wave by making marks at as many pointer locations on the circle as possible, and then translating these to instantaneous amplitudes, as exampled at A, B, C and D on the sine wave at the right-hand side of the diagram. It will be appreciated, of course, that in the diagram the sine wave starts with a positive-going half-cycle to point E, after which the negative-going half-cycle is traced out.

The sine wave is so called because the *sine* of the angle is equal to length XY divided by length OX. Length OX is fixed, so length XY (the wave's instantaneous amplitude) is a direct function of the sine of the angle. The angles are indicated along the sine wave for ease of identification.

Let us suppose that the instantaneous amplitude of the wave with the pointer at C (or at G in the negative direction), corresponding to the *peak amplitude*, is unity; then the amplitude with the pointer at B or D (or at F or H in the negative direction), corresponding to 45 degrees relative to the datum, is sin 45, or 0.707. This is an important value to keep in mind.

It is also noteworthy that a *cosine wave* can be constructed by basing the instantaneous amplitudes on the changing distance OY with changing angle.

The oscilloscope photo (oscillogram) in Figure 1.10(b) shows how a music wave differs from a sine wave. There is still an axis, often corresponding to zero, with positive- and negative-going components. Such a wave is far more complicated to analyse than a steady-state sine wave, though it can be resolved into a multiplicity of sine wave components. Complex waves of this nature are composed of many sine wave components added together in a special way to take account of not only their amplitudes but also their relative phases (that is, the relative 'timing' of the component waves).

A waveform, such as in Figure 1.9(b) or 1.10(a), can represent either current or voltage. The voltage is the alternating voltage (commonly referred to as a.c. voltage) that appears across a resistor, for example, when it is passing alternating current. In this sense it would be the potential difference. It could, of course, also be the source e.m.f.; for example, the output of an alternator (a.c. generator) off-load.

Average power

When a.c. is passed through a resistance, power is dissipated, just as when d.c. is passing. However, in order to calculate the power in the circuit we must use a suitable voltage reference on the waveform. Figure 1.11 reveals clearly that the instantaneous value of the voltage is a function of the wave shape. The question arises, therefore, whether we should use the peak value or some other value.

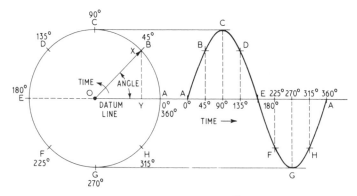

Figure 1.11. The formation of a sine wave – see text for description

Let us suppose that the d.c. passing through a 50-ohm resistor gives rise to 100 V across the resistor (from the particular source). As we have seen, the power dissipated by the resistor will be V^2/R, which is $100^2/50$, i.e. 200 W. The resistor will rise in temperature.

Now the a.c. voltage required to produce an equivalent temperature rise (or heating effect) is equal to the *r.m.s. value* of the sine wave (also called the *effective value*), which corresponds to 0.707 times the wave's peak voltage. Thus if the peak value of the sine wave is, say, 25 V, its r.m.s. or effective value will be 17.675 V. Conversely, the peak value can be found by multiplying the r.m.s. or effective value by 1.414. The precise multiplication factors are respectively $1/\sqrt{2}$ and $\sqrt{2}$.

R.M.S. stands for *root mean square*, and the value is obtained by working out the square root of the sum of all the instanteous values of the wave after they have been squared. There is no need to go to all this trouble, since with a sine wave the r.m.s. value is always equal to its peak value divided by $\sqrt{2}$. The peak value of a waveform is always greater than its r.m.s. value, except with a square wave, where the peak and r.m.s. values are equal.

However, it is very important to remember that most a.c. voltmeters are scaled in r.m.s. values *based on a sinewave input*. Thus should the waveform deviate from a sine wave, the reading will be inaccurate. The meter, in fact, usually responds to the *average* (see below and Figure 1.12) value of the waveform.

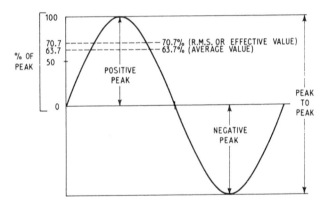

Figure 1.12. The parameters of a sine wave. The *form factor* of a waveform is the ratio of the r.m.s. value to the average value, which is 1.11 for a true sine wave (see text). The *crest factor* is the ratio of the peak value to the r.m.s. value (e.g. 1.414 for a sine wave)

Now back to the power bit. If the 100 V a.c. across the 50-ohm resistor is the r.m.s. voltage, then, as with 50 V d.c. across the resistor, the power dissipated will be 200 W. This is called the *average power*. If we calculate on the peak value of the 100 V r.m.s., we shall obtain the *peak power*, which is exactly twice the average power. For example, $100^2 \times \sqrt{2}^2/50$ equals 400 W *peak*. Peak power does not mean very much in radio or electrical work. What we need to know is the average power which is based on the r.m.s. values of voltage *and* current. As with d.c., their product also gives the power.

Figure 1.12 defines the various parameters of a sine wave. The peak value is from the zero datum line to either the positive or negative peak (with a pure sine wave the positive and negative peaks are equal); the peak-to-peak value is obviously twice the peak value; the r.m.s. or effective value is 70.7 per cent of the peak (not the peak-to-peak); and finally the *average value*, which is 63.7 per cent of the peak value. This has nothing to do with the average power. It is the value to which many rectifier-type a.c. meters respond. That is why, when such a meter is scaled in r.m.s. values based on a sine wave, and the input being measured deviates from a sine wave, the reading will not be the r.m.s. value of the waveform. The r.m.s. value of a sine wave is 1.11 times the average of the instantaneous values. The ratio of the r.m.s. value to the average value is called the *form factor*. As we have just seen, it is 1.11 for a sine wave (also for a full-wave-rectified sine wave). It is 1 for a true square wave; 1.41 for a half-wave-rectified square wave; 1.15 for a triangular wave (isosceles); 1.63 for a half-wave-rectified triangular wave; and 1.57 for a half-wave-rectified sine wave.

These examples give some idea of the error to be expected from an average responding meter when the waveform departs from a true sine wave. The average value of a sine wave of 100 V peak is 63.7 V. If this input is fed to an a.c. meter scaled in r.m.s. volts, the meter will indicate 70.7 V.

A.C. is produced by an alternator or oscillator; it also represents audio-frequency signals, as we have seen, but then of course it is usually quite different from a sine wave. When we talk of 240 V mains, we automatically assume the r.m.s. value is meant (not the peak, peak-to-peak or average value). Indeed, the peak-to-peak value of 240 V mains is around 678 V, the peak value being half of this. Little wonder, then, that the mains can give a hefty electric shock!

When 240 V mains is applied to an electric fire, for

example, the power drawn is the average power, which is the product of the r.m.s. voltage and r.m.s. current. This is because the load of an electric fire or similar item, including a bulb, is essentially resistive. Loads containing capacitance and inductance, as well as resistance, modify the power drawn. This important part of a.c. theory, which is very significant in radio, is discussed in Chapters 5 and 6.

When two or more waveforms are out of step with each other, there is said to be a *phase difference* between them. This is a timing difference which is measured in degrees. Let's suppose there are just two waves and that they start at exactly the same time from zero, build up to peak at the same time and fall back to zero again at the same time, then they would be in perfect phase.

However, should one start from zero when the other is at peak, then there would be a 90-degree phase difference between them. You can see why this is so by looking again at Figure 1.11. Phase opposition implies a difference of 180 degrees. That is when they are timed so that the peak of one occurs at the opposite peak of the other.

Such waveforms of equal amplitude would cancel each other. Total amplitude of two signals added together depends not only on the respective amplitudes of the two but also on their phase difference. When the phase difference is 90 degrees, the total amplitude can be determined by the vector sum. For example, if the amplitude of one is x volts and the other y volts, the total amplitude would be $\sqrt{(x^2 + y^2)}$. This can be determined geometrically using a phasor diagram, as can also the total amplitude at different phase angles. Only when two alternating waveforms are in phase can the total amplitude be determined by adding the amplitude of the two together directly.

Magnetism

Let us now conclude this chapter with a brief look at some of the more important aspects of magnetism. We all know the effects of magnetism; that a magnet has two poles (north and south); that when pivoted the north pole always points to the Earth's magnetic north; that magnets attract certain metal objects; that two magnets with their north and south poles approaching each other repel, while strong attraction is exhibited between unlike poles, this being akin to the electric laws of like charges repelling and unlike ones attracting.

A magnet can be produced by pointing a steel rod to the Earth's magnetic north and striking the rod a number of times with a wooden mallet, an exercise that tends to bring into alignment the molecules of the steel (see Figure 1.13).

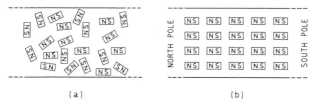

(a)   (b)

Figure 1.13. The molecules in unmagnetised metal can be regarded as being in random magnetic orientation, as shown at (a). When magnetised the molecules are pulled into magnetic alignment, as shown at (b)

A more potent method is to place the steel rod in the magnetic field produced by passing an electric current (d.c.) through a coil of wire. When the field is caused gradually to decay on switching off the current, the steel rod will exhibit all the effects of a magnet. This is called a *permanent magnet*. All such magnets are made in this way with various materials, including cobalt, tungsten and iron-oxide-processed ceramic, which is the material of some of the most recent permanent magnets.

An *electromagnet* consists of a soft iron core surrounded by many turns of wire. When current flows through the winding the soft iron core becomes a magnet of a strength depending on the number of turns of wire and the strength of the current flowing. When the current is switched off, the core loses its magnetism because the softness of the iron allows the molecules to revert to their random state of orientation.

The basic principle underlining this is revealed in Figure 1.13. A number of theories concerning the magnetic effect have been expounded over the years, but that illustrated in the diagram is logical and easily understood.

Flux and force lines

Although invisible under normal conditions, all magnets produce *lines of force*; such lines emanating from the classic horseshoe magnet are shown in Figure 1.14. The lines of force can be detected by placing thin paper over the magnet and sprinkling iron filings on the top; the filings then arrange

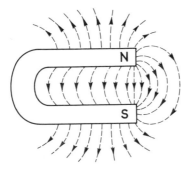

Figure 1.14. Magnetic lines of force emanating from a horseshoe magnet, showing the direction of the flux

themselves to the force pattern when the paper is tapped. A permanent record can be obtained by using waxed paper, heating the wax while gently tapping the paper to encourage the filings to orient themselves, and then allowing the wax to harden.

The term *magnetic field* or *flux* signifies that the space is threaded by the lines of force, the number of lines of force being a measure of magnetic strength. The term *lines of induction* also refers to the lines of force, but indicating both the strength *and* the direction of the flux (i.e. by the arrow heads from north to south, as in Figure 1.14).

In the SI system of units, the unit of magnetic flux is the weber (symbol Wb), while the unit of flux density is the tesla (symbol T), which is webers per square metre (Wb/m^2).

When a current flows through a conductor a magnetic field is created, and the field surrounding a straight conductor is shown in Figure 1.15. When the current is flowing towards an observer, the field is clockwise. A much more concentrated

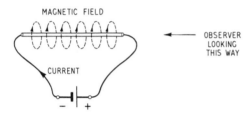

Figure 1.15. The magnetic flux produced by a straight conductor carrying current

field is produced when the conductor forms a coil (solenoid) of many turns of wire. The strength of the field increases when iron or steel forms the core instead of free space. The term *ferromagnetic* means that the *permeability* (the ratio of magnetic flux density in a material to the magnetising force applied to it) of the core material is much greater than that of free space, and that it varies with the flux density. The field produced by a coil of wire is shown in Figure 1.16.

The term *magnetomotive force* is often used in electro-magnetic engineering for the estimation of the flux produced by a given circuit. As electric current results from the source e.m.f., so magnetic flux results from the current flowing in a conductor. The magnetomotive force (m.m.f.) yielded by a solenoid of *N* turns passing *I* current is $F = NI$ ampere-turns. At a given point in the free-space field the m.m.f. per unit length (the magnetising force H) yields a flux density of $B_0 = \mu_0 H$, where $\mu_0 = 4/10^7$. When the core has permeability μ, the flux density is $B = \mu H$. Permeability of a material is governed by its chemical composition, heat treatment, mechanical stress and temperature, and is often affected by the flux density (i.e. the permeability changes with flux density, so the density is not directly proportional to the magnetising force).

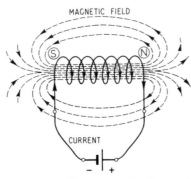

Figure 1.16. The magnetic lines of force yielded by a solenoid passing electric current

Materials with a relative permeability slightly less than that of a vacuum are called *diamagnetic; paramagnetic* is the term used when the permeability is slightly greater than unity, while the term *ferromagnetic* implies that the flux density does not follow the magnetising force, though such materials may exhibit very high permeabilities, up to 10 000 or so.

Figure 1.17 shows the cycle of magnetisation, or *hysteresis curve*, as it is often called. When the material is magnetically neutral and H is increased positively, B increases as described by line ab. When H is reduced back to zero, B fails to follow the original curve back to a, but traces line bc, so that even at zero H appreciable B remains, which corresponds to the induced magnetism. When H is increased negatively, B decreases as described by curve cd, where at d the material is effectively demagnetised. When H is further increased negatively, *B* increases likewise, effectively giving a polarity change, as described by curve de, where at e the material is again 'fully' magnetised. At f, *H* is once again zero, and as *H* increases in the positive direction, so *B* falls, first along fg and finally along gb, the cycle repeating.

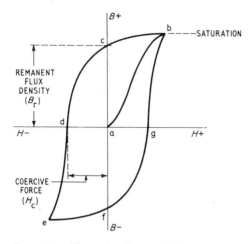

Figure 1.17. The cycle of magnetisation, or hysteresis curve (see text)

Different materials exhibit different characteristics, but it is worth noting four primary aspects of the process. First there is the *saturation* of the material, which is signified when an increase in *H* fails to increase *B* (i.e. when the material is incapable of acquiring any more magnetism). Second is the obvious *non-linearity*, displayed by equal increments of *H* failing to provide equal increments of *B*. Third is the *remanent induction* (B_r) remaining in the material after removal of *H*. The fourth has to do with the ability of the medium to retain its magnetism when the field is removed or its polarity changed. The force required to reduce the remanent induction to zero is called the coercive force (H_c). Its value depends on the *coercivity* of the medium as well as on the strength of the original induction.

Dynamo effect

A steady flux is produced when the current flowing through a solenoid or conductor is d.c. This rises to a maximum when the current is switched on, and decays when the current is switched off. When the current is reversed, the field polarity reverses. Each time the current is switched on and off, the increasing and decaying lines of force cut the conductor or the turns on a coil and slow down the rise and decay of the current.

This happens because, whenever magnetic lines of force cut across a conductor, an e.m.f. is developed in the conductor, and current flows when the circuit is completed. For example, take a coil of wire connected across a sensitive current-detecting instrument, and swiftly push one end of a bar magnet into the coil. The pointer of the instrument will 'kick', indicating a momentary current flow. When the magnet is equally as swiftly pulled out of the coil, the pointer will deflect in the opposite direction, indicating a change in direction of current. The direction is also changed by using a different end of the magnet or coil. No current is detected when the magnet is stationary. This demonstrates the *dynamo effect*, which is another way of producing electricity.

Motor effect

Conversely, when a magnet is arranged so that its field cuts a conductor passing current, a mechanical force results from the interaction of the two fields. This is called the *motor effect*. The direction of force reverses when the field of the magnet or the direction of the current is reversed.

In summary, then, electricity can be produced by expending mechanical energy, while mechanical energy can be produced by expending electricity. Dynamos are designed to produce either d.c. or a.c. (in the latter case the term alternator is more applicable); and similarly, electric motors can be designed to operate from either d.c. or a.c.

The dynamo effect is also exploited on a much smaller

scale for the production of signal voltages by the microphone (sound pressure waves causing movement of a conductor in a magnetic field), the gramophone pickup (groove vibrations supplying the mechanical energy by way of the spinning record), the tape head (the motor driving the magnetised tape contributing the mechanical requirement), etc.

The motor effect is not only responsible for operating electrical machinery, it also provides the acoustical output from the loudspeakers attached to radio receivers, amplifiers and so forth. In this case the cone or diaphragm is caused to vibrate in sympathy with the information carried by the signal current passing through a coil operating in a magnetic field.

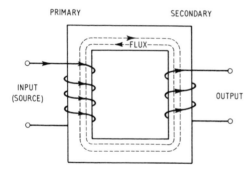

Figure 1.18. A transformer consists of primary and secondary windings on a core whose flux encloses both windings. A 'perfect' transformer would have resistance-less coils, a common magnetic circuit of infinite permeability and zero losses in the core. Although there is no such ideal, the practical transformer of good design has a high efficiency. The e.m.f. induced into the secondary is a function of both the input e.m.f. and the turns ratio between primary and secondary. A transformer is also used for matching one circuit to another, as well as for giving a voltage step-up or step-down at the secondary relative to the source

AC aspects

When a.c. is applied to a conductor or coil of wire, magnetic lines of force build up to maximum on one half-cycle, fall to zero at the middle of the two half-cycles, and then build up to an opposite field maximum on the other half-cycle. The resulting continuously changing magnetic field induces a back e.m.f. into the winding (coil, solenoid, etc.) which tends to oppose the applied a.c., producing inductive reactance (Chapters 5 and 6).

Transformer

Since a.c. produces a changing flux, an e.m.f. from this changing flux can be induced into a second winding in proximity. This is how a transformer works. For optimum efficiency, the two coils are arranged on a common magnetic circuit, produced by the design of the core; the coil to which the input is applied is called the *primary* , and that delivering the output, the *secondary* (see Figure 1.18). Transformers are important components in radio, as well as power engineering, and are considered in Chapter 6.

2

Radio signals

Radio waves are of the *electromagnetic wave* family, and they differ from light, heat, X-ray, cosmic, etc. radiation only in terms of wavelength. The wavelength of a sine wave is

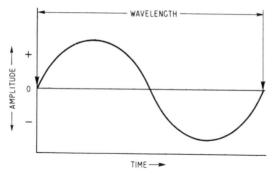

Figure 2.1. A radio signal can be represented by a sine wave, whose overall length of one complete cycle corresponds to the wavelength. Since the wave propagation velocity is constant at virtually 300×10^6 metres per second, the frequency can be found by dividing the velocity by the wavelength in metres; conversely, the wavelength can be found by dividing the velocity by the frequency in hertz

defined in Figure 2.1, and as most radio *information* is carried on a sine wave, this definition is perfectly applicable to radio signals.

While electricity requires a conducting medium (i.e.

current carriers) through which to travel, electromagnetic waves have the ability to travel through virtually anything (as dictated by their wavelength), including space. In the early days of 'wireless' it was considered (now seemingly with some justification!) that an invisible substance permeating the whole of the universe was responsible for the 'conduction' of radio waves. This was termed 'ether'. In his writings around the early nineteen-hundreds. Guglielmo Marconi made references to 'etheric waves'. However, it was Hertz, before Marconi, who showed that 'electric waves', when radiated into space, could be detected by a metal hoop at a distance from the source. The metal hoop was terminated by a small spark-gap, the gap producing minute electric sparks each time the transmitter was operated. It was Marconi, though, who thought of the idea of adopting 'Hertzian waves', as they were then sometimes called, for transmitting messages through space, and it was from these very early beginnings that radio as we know it today evolved. There were a number of radio pioneers who were responsible, individually or collectively, for furthering the mood of the day and for providing the information necessary for subsequent developments.

Our universe is sometimes said to function within a system governed by inertia, and to be itself composed of smaller systems – such as the orbiting electrons round the nucleus of atoms, the Earth's rotation round its axis, the rotation of the Earth round the sun, the movement of the solar system in our galaxy, etc. An inertia system is associated with mass or matter of some kind, and when energy is associated with mass, the speed of electromagnetic waves is constant, working out close to 300×10^6 metres per second, or 300 metres per micro-second (μs).

Science fiction often talks of 'mass-less' energy, where velocity of propagation is not limited to that of electromagnetic waves. Indeed, some people seriously consider the probability of a kind of energy operating outside the inertia system of our universe as we know it. The mathematics of relativity imply that mass goes infinite when accelerated beyond the constant velocity of electromagnetic waves.

32

Although this seems impossible, it could be that there is a breakaway of 'pure energy' (i.e. a release from mass) at this threshold value. There are a number of happenings, such as thought-transference for one, that appear to have no electromagnetic-wave association, and that might be more readily explained in terms of 'pure-energy', as distinct from energy associated with mass!

Frequency and wavelength

We are now widely deviating. To return to electromagnetic waves, since their velocity is constant at virtually 300×10^6 m/s, we can easily discover the wavelength by dividing 300×10^6 by the frequency of the wave in hertz, or the frequency by dividing 300×10^6 by the wavelength in metres. For

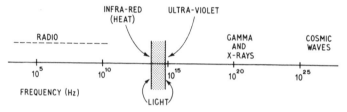

Figure 2.2. An impression of the electromagnetic wave spectrum

example, the wavelength of an electromagnetic wave in normal propagation of, say, 300 MHz (=300×10^6 Hz) is 1 m, while a wave of, say, 2 m has a frequency of $300 \times 10^6/2$, i.e. 150×10^6 Hz (=150 MHz). An idea of the electromagnetic wave spectrum is given in Figure 2.2, where the frequency is shown in hertz. Radio waves have the lowest frequencies and longest wavelengths, while cosmic waves have the highest frequencies and shortest wavelengths.

Radio wavebands

The long wave (l.w.) band extends from about 50 kHz (6000 m) to 600 kHz (500 m), the medium wave (m.w.) band from about 600 kHz to 1.5 MHz (200 m) and the short wave (s.w.) band overall from 1.5 MHz to 300 MHz (1 m).

Frequency classifications are also used, such as very low frequency (v.l.f.) from 3 to 30 kHz; low frequency (l.f.) from 30 to 300 kHz; medium frequency (m.f.) from 300 to 3000 kHz; high frequency (h.f.) from 3 to 30 MHz; very high frequency (v.h.f.) from 30 to 300 MHz; ultra high frequency (u.h.f.) from 300 to 3000 MHz; super high frequency (s.h.f.) from 3 to 30 GHz and extra high frequency (e.h.f.) from 30 to 3000 GHz.

Radio wave source

The type of electromagnetic wave used for radio is produced by an a.c. wave fed into an aerial and 'coupled', so to speak, to 'space'. This establishes an invisible wave motion, thereby yielding radio waves. The a.c. wave is commonly a pure sine wave, called a *carrier wave*, since its job is to carry information in the form of code, sound, pictures, etc.

The first electromagnetic wave energy (excluding that arriving from outer space, such as cosmic waves) was created by an electric spark or arc. Although this sort of emission has long been out of date so far as sending messages is concerned, it does still plague ordinary radio and television reception in the form of electrical interference. Whenever an electric spark or arc occurs, an interfering radio wave is sent into space, causing crackles on radio and flashes on television receivers within its range. Fortunately, the range is limited in most cases owing to the relatively small energy of the spark or arc and its inefficient coupling to space.

Nevertheless, radio and television reception can be badly impaired in areas close to such interference sources, such as large electric motors, industrial machinery, etc. Even domestic electrics can affect the reception unless the source is properly suppressed (that is, by taking steps to reduce the electromagnetic energy) which is now law. A typical example of this sort of electromagnetic emission and its effect on radio and television is a flash of lightning. We have all experienced the crackles on radio (particularly on the long and medium wave bands) and flashes on television when a thunderstorm is close at hand.

This is so-called *impulsive* emission of electromagnetic wave energy. If a spark or arc is continuous a radio receiver detects it as a continuous series of crackles or high-pitched buzz. By keying a spark transmitter it is possible to transmit coded messages.

However, for the transmission of sound (audio) and pictures (video) a 'smooth' continuous carrier wave is normally required; in other words, a sine wave. An oscillator produces a low-power sine wave of accurately controlled frequency, and this is stepped up to the required power by an amplifier, which is then coupled efficiently to an aerial (Chapter 4).

The waveform of a radio transmitter is similar to that produced by an a.c. generator, but while the latter has a frequency of 50–60 Hz, radio waves are of a very much higher frequency, as we have seen. If, for example, an a.c. power wave is coupled to a loudspeaker it is heard as a low-pitched hum. As the frequency is increased, so the pitch of the note rises until, at around 16 kHz, it changes from a very shrill note to a 'hiss' and then is heard no longer. From about 50 Hz downwards, the note gets deeper in pitch, and at around 16 Hz is felt rather than heard if it is powerful enough. At lower frequency the separate impulses may be audible. The range 16 Hz–16 kHz is the *audio spectrum*, where the energy is commonly converted into sound waves by a loudspeaker or headphones. Sound waves compress and rarefy the air according to the vibrations of the sounding source and cause our eardrums to vibrate in sympathy, so that we experience the sensation of sound.

Radio waves, of course, are not audible; they travel through space, while sound waves usually travel through air. Moreover, the velocity of propagation of sound waves through air at sea level and 20°C is close to 344 m/s, which is far, far slower than radio waves. Thus there is no direct connection between radio waves and sound waves, though the two types of waves are involved in radio transmission and reception.

Modulation

The information that the radio wave is required to carry needs to be superimposed in some way upon it. This is called *modulation*. However, even when a radio wave is modulated, it cannot be used directly in this form. For example, if an audio signal is superimposed on the carrier wave, a loudspeaker or headphones set receiving this signal, even after being greatly amplified, would fail to respond to it because, in spite of the modulation, the signal remains still at *radio frequency* (r.f.) and hence well above audibility. To reclaim the audio signal the modulated r.f. wave needs to be *demodulated*, a process that removes the carrier wave so that only the true audio signal remains. Demodulation, which is the reciprocal of modulation, is considered in Chapter 5.

The simplest way of modulating a carrier wave is to key it on and off in accordance with a code, such as Morse code, as shown in Figure 2.3, or radio teletype (RTTY). The first is called interrupted carrier wave (i.c.w. for short). The receiver

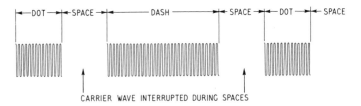

Figure 2.3. One method of transmitting a coded signal is by interrupting the carrier wave as shown. This is called interrupted carrier wave (i.c.w.) operation (see also Figure 2.8)

then receives bursts of signal which, after suitable processing, is rendered audible as a tone of dots, dashes and spaces. The second is a development of teleprinter radio communication, using instead a video display unit (v.d.u.) which has gained popularity with radio amateurs of recent years. The d.c. RTTY signal is sometimes used to frequency-modulate (see later) an audio oscillator by a 'shift' frequency corresponding to the difference between the mark and space states. This output is then fed to the modulator of the transmitter in place, for instance, of the microphone signal. the subject, however, is somewhat involved and interested readers would do well to gen up on the technique from the radio amateur books.

Sound modulation

With normal radio broadcasting, of course, sound information is modulated on to the carrier wave. Any sounding source produces weak variations in pressure around the nominal air pressure (details are given in the author's *The Audio Handbook,* published by Newnes Technical Books). The pressure variations, corresponding to the intensity (amplitude), frequency (pitch) and general nature of the sound, are propagated through the air, gradually weakening as they spread out, and are communicated to the eardrums of anyone in range, causing them to vibrate in sympathy with the sounding source. The vibrating eardrums in turn produce impulses which are interpreted by the brain as the sensation of hearing.

When a microphone responds to sound waves it yields a small electrical signal of an amplitude that corresponds to the intensity of the sound, a frequency that corresponds to the pitch, and general characteristics that correspond to the nature of the sound. If a tuning fork is sounded in front of a microphone, and the tuning fork is on a sounding board, an oscilloscope would display a sine wave when connected to the microphone signal, as shown in Figure 2.4. The frequency is a function of the design of the tuning fork; a middle-C tuned fork, for instance, has a frequency around 256 Hz, and a relatively pure sine wave occurs when the vibrating fork is held against a sounding board, which tends to amplify the fundamental frequency while attenuating overtones.

Few musical instruments give pure sine wave signals; most of them contain harmonic frequencies of the fundamental and overtones, which provide the characteristic sound or *timbre* of the instrument. This is true of all sounds, including

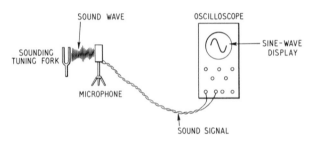

Figure 2.4. A sounding tuning fork produces an essentially 'pure' sine wave when held against a sounding board (this means that its harmonic and overtone content is small). When the fork is placed in front of a microphone, the microphone will deliver a sine wave signal. This can be displayed on the screen of an oscilloscope as shown

speech. The waveforms in Figure 1.10 show how a music signal differs from a pure sine wave signal.

The sound signal from the microphone, tape machine, gramophone pickup, etc. is amplified and possibly equalised before being introduced to the carrier wave.

Amplitude modulation

One method of modulating the carrier wave is for the audio signal to cause the amplitude of the carrier wave to vary. This is called *amplitude modulation* (a.m.). It is best to look at this in terms of a sine wave modulation signal, as illustrated in Figure 2.5. Here waveform (a) is the carrier, waveform (b) the sine-wave audio for modulating the carrier, and waveform (c) the resulting modulated carrier wave. It should be clearly understood that the frequency of the carrier wave remains constant. Only its amplitude is changed in accordance with the parameters of the modulation signal. The dotted outline of (c) is called the *modulation envelope*. The modulation *depth* depends on the amplitude of the modulation signal relative to the amplitude of the carrier wave, the modulation depth at (c) being defined by the ratio *B/A*. If the unmodulated amplitude of the carrier wave is, say, 1 V, 50 per cent modulation depth results in amplitude variations of the carrier from 0.5 V to 1.5 V; 100 per cent depth would cause the carrier to rise to 2 V on peaks and fall to zero volts at the troughs. A modulation signal of amplitude in excess of the requirement for 100 per cent depth would cause the carrier to fall to zero amplitude for a finite time and thus badly distort the transmission.

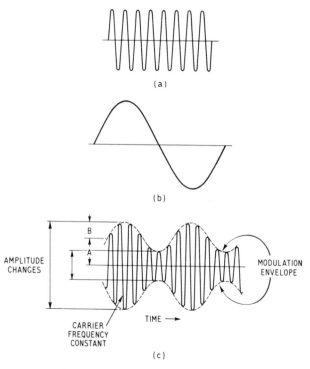

Figure 2.5. The principle of amplitude modulation (a.m.). When carrier wave (a) is amplitude-modulated by audio signal (b) the modulation waveform at (c) is produced

The process of amplitude modulation yields an upper and a lower *sideband* signal for each modulation frequency, and each sideband is separated from the carrier frequency by an amount equal to the modulation frequency. When a pure sine wave signal is used for modulation, there are just two sidebands, as shown in Figure 2.6. The amplitude of each sideband depends on the modulation depth; for 100 per cent modulation the amplitude of each sideband is half the amplitude of the carrier wave.

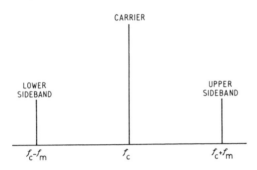

Figure 2.6. When a pure signal (sine wave) modulates a carrier wave, two additional components result on either side of the carrier. Here is shown carrier f_c modulated by sine wave f_m. The component below the carrier at $f_c - f_m$ is the lower sideband and that above the carrier at $f_c + f_m$ is the upper sideband

If the carrier frequency is, say, 100 kHz and the sine wave modulation frequency 1 kHz, then the lower sideband would fall at 100 − 1 kHz, i.e. 99 kHz, and the upper sideband at 100 + 1 kHz, i.e. 101 kHz. The signal would thus require an overall *passband* of 2 kHz to accommodate it. An interesting spectrogram taken at the author's laboratory is given in Figure 2.7. Here the large middle pulse represents a 50 MHz carrier, and the two smaller pulses on either side the lower and upper sidebands resulting from 10 kHz sine wave modulation. The horizontal divisions correspond approximately to 10 kHz. Thus the display reveals that each sideband is separated from the carrier by 10 kHz. To accommodate both sidebands, therefore, the passband would need to be 20 kHz.

40

Owing to the varying and transient nature of a music signal, one can imagine the complexity of the sidebands resulting from this kind of modulation signal. For maximum fidelity, the passband of the receiver must be sufficiently wide to avoid suppression of the higher-order sidebands, stemming from treble modulation frequencies. If there is suppression, then of course the treble reproduction is impaired.

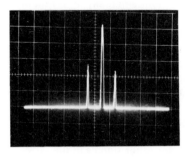

Figure 2.7. Spectrogram showing a 50 MHz carrier wave modulated by a 10 kHz sine wave. Each horizontal division corresponds approximately to 10 kHz, so the display reveals that the lower and upper sidebands are each separated from the carrier by 10 kHz

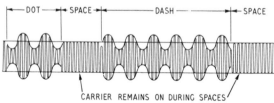

Figure 2.8. Amplitude-modulated tone is sometimes used for coded transmissions (see Figure 2.3)

Amplitude-modulation is also sometimes used for coded transmissions. In this case, the carrier remains on during the spaces, and the dots and dashes are provided by tone modulation, as shown in Figure 2.8.

Single-sideband modulation

As revealed by Figures 2.6 and 2.7, each modulation frequency gives rise to corresponding lower and upper sidebands. For proper processing, the ordinary type of broadcast receiver must pass on to the demodulator both sidebands to avoid distortion. This in turn means that the receiver must have a passband corresponding to twice the highest modulation frequency. In the crowded medium and short wave bands, this requirement can prove an embarrassment since there is the possibility of signals from adjacent unwanted stations passing through the receiver along with the wanted signal. This is fundamentally a problem of selectivity; but if the selectivity is made too sharp, then the higher-order sidebands are attenuated (Chapter 5).

There is a technique whereby one of the sidebands at the transmitter is suppressed and the demodulator at the receiver is designed in conjunction with an oscillator to reclaim the missing sideband. This is called *single-sideband* (s.s.b.) operation.

It will be appreciated that this technique cuts the amount of spectrum energy fed into the aerial by the transmitter, thereby leaving more room for other signals in the crowded 'airways'. Moreover, since the receiver needs to cater for only one sideband, its passband can be almost halved; this facilitates the design for improved selectivity, thereby reducing the probability of adjacent station interference.

Single-sideband operation is used mostly in the amateur bands; it is not used for general broadcasting. When a single-sideband transmission is tuned in on an ordinary broadcast receiver, the reception is very distorted. As already mentioned, receivers with facilities for reclaiming the missing sideband are required for correct reception of single-sideband transmissions. It is sometimes possible to obtain intelligible reception from an ordinary receiver by using an external oscillator to beat with the carrier at the receiver's demodulator. The single-sideband transmitter suppresses the carrier and deletes one of the sidebands, and because only the essential signals are radiated there is a substantial effective power gain. Moreover, from the communications point of view s.s.b. systems are favoured because they are less disturbed by changing propagations conditions than ordinary a.m. or f.m.

Frequency modulation

Another method of modulation causes the frequency of the carrier wave to vary above and below its mean frequency at a rate corresponding to the frequency of the modulation signal and by an amount (the *deviation*) corresponding to the amplitude of the modulation signal. Thus the higher the frequency of the modulation, the greater the rate of change of carrier frequency; and the greater the amplitude (i.e. the intensity of the sound) of the modulation, the greater the deviation either side of the carrier frequency. This is called *frequency-modulation* (f.m.), where the amplitude of the carrier remains constant.

Frequency-modulation is used in the v.h.f. band for high-quality audio transmissions; it is also used for the sound on 625-line television. Maximum deviation for radio broadcasting is ±75 kHz, and modulation frequencies as high as 15 kHz are carried by the system on mono, thereby ensuring outstanding fidelity (even higher modulation frequencies are used on stereo to cater for the stereo information – see Chapters 4 and 5).

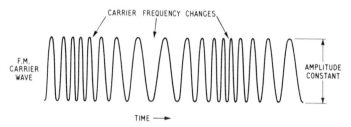

Figure 2.9. F.M. signal. The frequency is deviated either side of the mean carrier frequency at a rate corresponding to the frequency and by an amount corresponding to the amplitude of the modulation signal. The amplitude remains constant

An elementary impression of an f.m. signal is given in Figure 2.9. The sideband yield of f.m. is more complex than that of a.m. For each 'pure' modulation signal there is a series of pairs of sidebands separated from the carrier frequency by one, two, three, etc. times the modulation frequency. On music, therefore, the sideband structure becomes extremely complicated, where the modulation consists of a multiplicity of frequencies. The sideband structure is affected by both the modulation frequency and the deviation, this being indicated by the *modulation index*, which is equal to the frequency of deviation (f_d) divided by the frequency of modulation (f_m). The number of pairs of sidebands increases with the modulation index. Thus, with a given f_d, the number of pairs of sidebands increases with reducing f_m. Reciprocally, with a given f_m, the number increases with increasing f_d.

The higher-order pairs of sidebands diminish in amplitude, although some pairs may be of greater amplitude than the carrier, depending on f_d and f_m. An example of the sideband structure when f_m = 400 Hz and f_d = 1 kHz (i.e. modulation index = 2.5) is given in Figure 2.10. The spectrogram in Figure 2.11 gives an impression of the higher-amplitude sideband of an f.m. signal from the screen of a spectrum analyser (compare with the a.m. signal spectrogram in Figure 2.7).

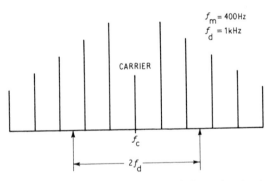

Figure 2.10. Sideband structure of f.m. signal of modulation index = 2.5 (see text)

The increased sideband content of f.m. means that a receiver bandwidth greater than that for a.m. must be made available if all the advantages of the f.m. system of entertainment broadcasting are to be achieved. On the wideband f.m. system, restriction of the receiver bandwidth results in harmonic distortion during loud passages of music. The advantages of f.m. over a.m. are considered in Chapter 5.

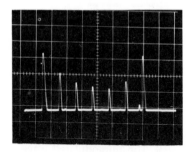

Figure 2.11. Spectrogram (taken by the author) of an f.m. signal, showing the higher-amplitude sidebands

Mention should be made that in the amateur bands the deviation is restricted to around 2.5 kHz to 3 kHz to avoid undue spread of the sidebands. This is narrow-band f.m. (n.b.f.m.) as distinct from the wide-band f.m. of entertaiment broadcasting where fidelity is more important than 'communications quality' within restricted spectrum space. Chapter 11 shows how f.m. is used with CB radio, but here the deviation requirement is even less than on the amateur bands (at 27 MHz at least) where a large number of channels need to be occupied within a very small slice of radio spectrum.

The additional information required for two-channel stereo broadcasting is also contained in the f.m. signal, and how this is achieved is revealed in Chapter 4.

So far, then, we have looked at some of the important radio signals. The next chapter tells how the signals are propagated through space and picked up by the receiving aerial.

3

Signal propagation and reception

Whether unmodulated or modulated, a radio wave can be regarded as the product of oscillatory energy coupled to space by the transmitting aerial. The unmodulated wave is the carrier wave which, when modulated, is the 'vehicle' upon which the required information is conveyed. The energy is of an electromagnetic nature, whose electric and magnetic fields alternate continuously in polarity, like the signal waveform that was responsible for the energy in the first place.

The alternating magnetic field creates and sustains the alternating electric field at right angles to it, rather like the 'dynamo effect' discussed in Chapter 1. Once launched, the wave continues travelling away from its source at the speed of light (about 300 metres per millionth of a second) until all its energy is exhausted.

It is noteworthy that a radio wave (or electromagnetic wave – e.m. wave) is called a *transverse* wave because the electric and magnetic components are perpendicular to each other *and* to the direction of wave travel. This is distinct from the *longitudinal sound wave* whose supporting particles vibrate in the same direction as the wave travels.

Signal field

The presence of a radio wave continuously emanating from the transmitting aerial gives rise to a *signal field*, whose intensity is obviously greatest close to the aerial, progressively

46

diminishing with distance from it. The *energy flux* (that is, the rate of flow of energy through a surface of unit area) is the product of the electric field E and the magnetic field H, this being true for a plane wave in free space, when E and H are in phase, which occurs as the wave spreads away from the aerial. Close to the transmitting aerial the electric and magnetic fields alternate 90 degrees out of phase with each other, but at such close proximity the wave cannot then be regarded as a plane wave.

In homogeneous space, radio waves travel in straight lines, which is akin to light propagation, until they encounter a solid object. Like light, radio waves are influenced by reflection, refraction and diffraction. The rate at which the intensity of the signal diminishes as the distance from the source increases is related to its rectilinear propagation mode. The law of inverse squares is involved, which states that the intensity varies inversely as the square of the distance from the source.

Under practical conditions many other factors come into play, including reflection, refraction, diffraction and partial 'blocking' by earthy objects, such as large buildings, hills, trees and so forth, depending on the wavelength of the wave.

The field strength round a transmitting station is given either in terms of microvolts per metre (μV/m) or in decibels (dB), where the zero-decibel datum corresponds to $1\,\mu$V. Thus a signal field given as 60 dB would imply a strength of 60 dB above $1\,\mu$V. 60 dB corresponds to a voltage ratio of 1000:1, so in this example the field strength would be 1000 μV or 1 mV.

The decibel is commonly used in radio and audio work, and it is nothing more than a logarithmic unit representing a *ratio*. The decibel value is equal to the logarithm of a *voltage ratio multiplied by twenty*, or of a *power ratio multiplied by ten*. Calculation is rarely necessary since detailed decibel tables are readily available.

The signal field links with a receiving aerial, and into this is then induced a much smaller replica of the alternating signal fed to the transmitting aerial that started the radio waves in the first place.

Wave analogy

It is difficult to describe a radio wave and signal field; but if such a wave approaching an observer could be made visible, its electric and magnetic fields might resolve as shown in Figure 3.1.

A good analogy is given in Figure 3.2. The oscillatory energy from a transmitting aerial coupled into space gives

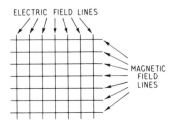

ELECTRIC FIELD LINES

MAGNETIC FIELD LINES

Figure 3.1. Elementary impression of a wave front approaching an observer. A wave is said to be polarised in the direction of the electric vector, which means that the wave illustrated is vertically polarised, such that a vertically-mounted aerial is required to receive it fully (see later text)

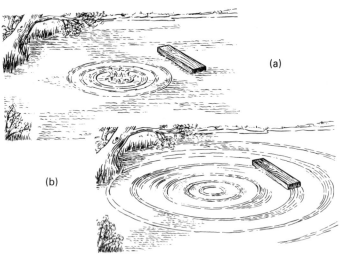

(a)

(b)

Figure 3.2. (a) Water-wave analogy of a radio wave. (b) A piece of wood floating on the water is caused to move up and down by the wave action; this is similar in effect to the signal induced into a receiving signal field, which is here represented by the waves spreading out from the source

rise to radio waves which, from an elementary viewpoint, can be likened to the waves that spread out from a pool of calm water when it is disturbed by the throwing in of a stone, as shown by (a) of the diagram. Like radio waves, the water waves gradually diminish in amplitude (strength) as they spread further from the source. The water does not move outwards to generate the waves; the action is a simple rise and fall. A wave already formed yields a new, weaker and greater diameter wave, and so on, until there is no energy left to form further waves. This, of course, is only a two-dimensional analogy; radio waves in space are three-dimensional. That is, the signal field expands as a sphere from the aerial, though this may be modified by the directional effects of the transmitting aerial.

When the first wave in Figure 3.2(a) reaches the floating wood, the wood is caused to rise and fall with the wave motion, and a continuous rising and falling motion results when the waves surround the wood, as shown at (b). The water represents the space in which the radio waves expand, the kinetic energy released at the impact of the stone on the water represents the oscillatory energy at the transmitting aerial, the amplitude of the waves represents the signal field, and the wood motion represents the signal induced into the receiving aerial as the result of the signal field. The greater the amplitude of the waves (the signal field), the greater the amplitude of oscillation of the wood (the received signal).

The energy of the signal induced into the receiving aerial is millions of times smaller than the energy of the signal fed to the transmitting aerial from the power amplifier of the transmitter. The transmitter power may be thousands of watts, while the effective power fed to the receiver from the aerial may be in the order of a millionth of a watt or less. Space, then, is not a very efficient conveyer of energy.

Aerial gain and directivity

The amount of signal energy actually launched into space depends not only on the power of the transmitter, but also on the effective *amplification* or *gain* of the transmitting aerial. The directionality of the aerial is here brought into account. If it is required to radiate the radio signal in all directions from the transmitting aerial, the aerial is designed to possess what is known as an *omnidirectional* polar diagram. The radio waves then emanate in the form of an expanding sphere from it. This may well be wasteful of signal energy. For example, it may not be required to radiate the

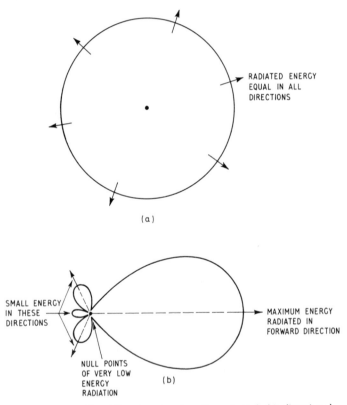

Figure 3.3. (a) Omnidirectional polar diagram and (b) directional polar diagram. Although drawn in two dimensions, the diagrams in reality have a three-dimensional characteristic

signals skywards at too high an angle, or in a specific direction that is catered for by a different transmitter or that has only open sea.

In these cases, the transmitting aerial is designed to concentrate its radiation in one or more directions, with nulls in the other direction. Such an aerial is said to be directional, and would thus exhibit a *directional* polar diagram. Figure 3.3 shows at (a) an omnidirectional polar diagram and at (b) a directional polar diagram; but again it should be remembered that these are three-dimensional in reality, although shown in two-dimensional form in the diagrams. The directionality pattern of (b) can be arranged to suit any requirement that may be dictated by the topography or transmitter-coverage specification.

By concentrating the radiated energy into a specific direction or directions, the effect is tantamount to having a greater transmitted power in that or those direction(s). The aerial is thus said to have *gain* over an omnidirectional aerial in that or those particular directions. It is also possible, by stacking and phasing certain types of aerial, to achieve effective omnidirectional gain, but at the expense of skyward radiation (which may not be required, anyway), the polar diagram then being after the style of a squashed cottage loaf.

The gain of an aerial is generally stated in decibels. An aerial with a 6 dB power gain, for example, would provide a 4:1 power step up, so when coupled to a 50 kW transmitter would yield an *effective radiated power* (e.r.p.) of 200 kW on its main beam.

Propagation

The wavelength of the signal affects its propagation. U.H.F. and v.h.f. waves, which are of relatively short wavelength, are more easily reflected from large buildings, hills, etc. than waves of lower frequency and hence longer wavelength. Long and medium wave signals have the ability to evoke a substantial signal field at the far side of such obstructions, while v.h.f. and u.h.f. signals (in particular) may be almost completely blocked by them. Indeed, u.h.f. reception may be rendered virtually impossible at a site screened from the transmitting aerial by a large hill.

As the frequency is increased and the wavelength reduced, the wave tends to conform more to the rules governing light propagation and less to the rules of medium-wave propagation. Waves of small length are reflected fairly easily by objects in their line of travel, and when the obstruction is not smaller than about one wavelength it behaves in rather the same way that a mirror behaves to light rays. Waves at the lower end of the v.h.f. band are somewhat less affected in this way owing to the relatively longer wavelength, smaller obstructions then presenting less of a problem to them. It is possible for a signal to appear behind an obstruction as the wavelength is increased, owing to *diffraction* of the wave over its surfaces.

Radio signals of long wavelength are affected even less by obstructions, and are capable of producing behind an obstruction a signal field of an intensity almost equal to that of the signal field in front. It is well known, of course, that medium and long wave transmissions are adequately received by indoor aerials, such as the ferrite-rod aerials (see page 63) used in transistor radios.

Medium-frequency propagation

Two main types of wave are concerned in long, medium and short wave broadcasting. These are known as the *sky wave* and the *ground wave*. A further manifestation of the sky wave is involved in v.h.f. and u.h.f. broadcasting, this being commonly termed the *space wave*.

The ground wave progressively diminishes in strength with distance from the transmitter, owing to spreading and earth-absorption effects; the latter, stem from earth-induced signal field charges, the degree of loss depending upon the nature of the ground along the signal path and the signal wavelength (the losses increase with increasing frequency). What happens is that the wave induces charges in the earth, and as they travel along with the wave they constitute an energy-dissipating current. That portion of the wave which lies in contact with the earth, therefore, is continuously having its energy removed and replaced by diffraction of energy from that part of the wave which lies directly above the earth. Net results are attenuation, as already noted, coupled with cancellation of any horizontal polarisation and a wave front with a slight forward tilt.

Ionosphere

The sky wave passes through the Earth's local atmosphere and enters the *ionosphere*. The ionosphere is a part of the Earth's outer atmosphere where free electrons are normally present in quantities sufficient to modify the propagation of radio waves passing through it. There are three primary regions, the D region abut 50–90 km above the Earth's surface, the E region about 90–150 km and the F region about 150 km and above. During daylight hours the F region divides into two layers – the lower called F_1 and the higher F_2. The D layer is essentially present only during the daylight hours, and in essence this also applies to the E layer, though somewhat less active E layer presence is sometimes detected at night. However, because of the fairly speedy recombination of the ions at the lower altitudes, the E and D regions can only hold a significant degree of ionisation when in sunlight.

On arriving at the ionosphere, the oblique path of the medium-frequency wave is refracted (an analogy being the bending of light rays due to propagation through a lens, piece of glass, water, etc.) such that the wave is put on an Earth-return path. The wave returns to Earth at a distance from the transmitter related to its angle of departure on its sky-bound journey, to the nature and height of the ionospheric layer responsible for the 'bending', and to the frequency (wavelength) of the transmission.

The sky wave might well return to Earth at a considerable

distance from the transmitter, which is the principle of long-distance radio reception, as shown in Figure 3.4. Here is shown (in broken line) the ground wave, which hugs the surface of the Earth and which fairly swiftly attenuates, and (in solid line) the sky wave, which returns to Earth beyond the range of the ground wave by the *refractive* influence of the ionosphere.

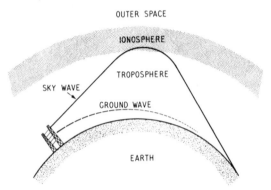

Figure 3.4. The ground wave fades owing to absorption, while the sky wave is deflected back to Earth by the ionosphere, thereby yielding a signal field at distances in advance of the ground wave

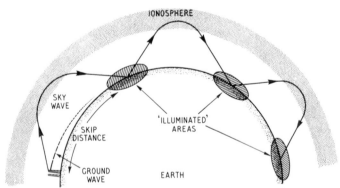

Figure 3.5. Signal hops between the Earth and the ionosphere are responsible for long-distance medium-frequency reception

At particular frequencies and times the sky wave is 'reflected' almost or completely round the planet by reflection from the ionosphere to Earth and from the Earth back to the ionosphere a number of times, as illustrated in Figure 3.5. It will be noticed that the reception at the 'illuminated' zones round the planet results essentially from the returned sky wave, the ground wave having faded out. This means that there are substantial areas between each 'skip' where there is no or very little signal field. These are called *skip distance* areas. It is noteworthy that the maxima of a layer may not be at its centre, nor does the ionisation vanish completely between layers.

Radio fading

If the sky wave happens to return to Earth at a point where there is still a field due to the ground wave, as shown in Figure 3.6, the receiving aerial then responds to the energy of both waves. When the waves are in phase the total energy is

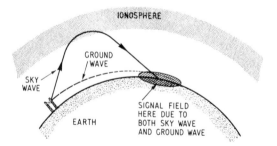

Figure 3.6. Fading results from a signal field compounded from sky waves and ground waves (see text)

added, but when there is lack of phase-coincidence some degree of energy cancellation results (see page 22).

As the refractive index of the ionosphere changes, the phase and strength of the returned sky wave change too. In reaction with the ground-wave field, this results in variations in the net signal field at the receiving point, which is one cause of *radio fading*.

The layers of the ionosphere tend to vary both in refractive index and in height above the Earth, depending on the time of day and night and season of the year. The layers are influenced by radiations from outer space and from the sun, which is the reason for the cyclic 24-hour sequence. This is also the reason why long-distance reception (sometimes called *DX reception*), especially on the short wavebands, is affected by the time of day or night, and why the low wavelength (high-frequency) end of the medium waveband becomes more active from dusk onwards

This enhancement stems from the fact that the D layer fades out after sunset. During the daytime it almost completely absorbs m.f. skybound signals owing to inelastic collisions between the free electrons and the ionised and neutral atoms of the lower atmosphere when they are excited by the radio waves. Thus, during the daytime reception is confined virtually to the ground wave, but after sunset the m.f. skywaves are subjected to refraction by the higher layers since they are not then cut off by the D layer.

Radio fade-out

The nature and density of the ionospheric layers influence wave refraction at different frequencies, and as they change, so waves of different frequency are more influenced; that is why it is necessary to choose the wavelength for long-distance propagation depending on the time of day or night. The time of year also affects the nature of the ionosphere, and hence radio propagation, as also can storms in the ionosphere.

Storms on the sun (sunspot activity) can also increase the refractive property of the upper layers to higher frequencies. As the frequency of a wave is increased so it penetrates more deeply into the upper layers and hence is reflected back to earth from a more elevated point. At a given frequency, while taking account of the angle of radiation, it penetrates the layer completely and vanishes into space. This frequency is related to the *maximum usable frequency* (m.u.f.) at the time, the m.u.f. increasing during sunspot maximum and decreasing during sunspot minimum, which follows an approximate 11-year cycle.

The *critical frequency* relates to the frequency of signal returned by the ionosphere when the radiation is directly upwards from the Earth, being approximately three to four times lower than the m.u.f. for a long oblique path.

A so-called *radio fade-out* (otherwise known as Dellinger fade-out) results from an ionospheric disturbance such that the ionisation in the D layer is increased abnormally so that the h.f. waves which would normally pass through are absorbed, although the disturbance is usually short-lived. An ionospheric storm is characterised by a general deterioration in propagation conditions in the band from about 3 MHz to 30 MHz. A magnetic storm, which is a major disturbance of the Earth's magnetic field, generally lasting for one or more days, affects at least one of the components of a radio field.

Long-wave propagation relies almost entirely on the ground wave. The sky wave comes more into effect from the medium waveband upwards. At the lower wavelengths and higher frequencies, the ground wave is swiftly attenuated by Earth losses (absorption).

V.H.F. and u.h.f. propagation

Under normal conditions v.h.f. and u.h.f. waves pass through the ionosphere into the space beyond. However, waves of such frequency are more influenced by the Earth's local atmosphere, referred to as the *troposphere*, than longer wavelength waves. The troposphere is the lower part of the Earth's atmosphere extending upwards from the Earth's surface to a ceiling of around 10 km; in this region the temperature decreases with height at the rate of 6°/km down to about −55°C, except in local layers of temperature inversion, where temperature increases with height.

V.H.F. and u.h.f. transmitting aerials are engineered to exploit the so-called *space wave*, which is somewhat analogous to a ray of light emanating from the top of a lighthouse, except for the difference in wavelength, of course! Light rays, owing to their very small wavelength, are less affected by the troposphere than v.h.f. and u.h.f. radio waves. The latter are more easily refracted by the troposphere, and tend to hug the Earth's surface over limited distances, as illustrated in Figure 3.7.

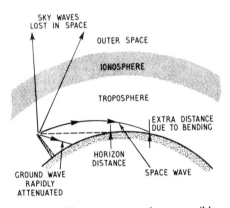

Figure 3.7. The space wave is responsible for v.h.f. and u.h.f. reception. This exceeds the line-of-sight distance between the transmitting and receiving aerials owing to tropospheric refraction (bending). The ground wave is quickly attenuated by Earth losses, and under normal reception condition the sky wave penetrates the ionosphere and continues its non-communicating journey into space

The 'bending' effect tends to diminish with increasing frequency, which means that the normal propagation distance is a little less at u.h.f. than at v.h.f. Were the waves not so influenced, v.h.f. and u.h.f. propagation would be limited to the optical horizon distances between the tops of the transmitting and receiving aerials. The tropospheric 'bending' extends the *radio horizon*, thereby providing a greater distance of coverage by the space waves.

Under normal conditions the nominal refractive index of the troposphere has the effect of increasing the Earth's radius so far as radio signals are concerned. The refractive index is affected by local weather conditions, but the nominal refractive index is based on the ratio 4/3 with respect to the Earth's radius. The *optical horizon* distance in statute miles is $\sqrt{(1.5\,h)}$, where h is the elevation in feet, which puts the *radio horizon*, based on the nominal index, at $\sqrt{(2\,h)}$ miles. Thus it is seen that v.h.f. and u.h.f. coverage is significantly affected by the height of the transmitting and receiving aerials (see later). The power of the transmitter, of course, comes into account, but this has *less* influence on range-limit signal fields than aerial height.

In the general case, the strength of the signal field is directly proportional to the height and to the *square root* of the e.r.p. of the transmitter, and inversely proportional to the wavelength and to the square of the distance.

Some of the space waves emanating from a v.h.f. or u.h.f. transmitting aerial must obviously strike the earth, as shown in Figure 3.8. Some of the wave energy is absorbed by the Earth and some is reflected back to the sky. The space wave is

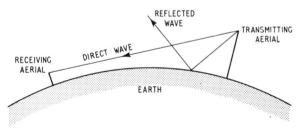

Figure 3.8. The direct or space wave is responsible for v.h.f. and u.h.f. reception, and the receiving aerial is usually below the influence of the Earth-reflected wave

a combination of the direct and ground-reflected waves (the latter, of course, is different from the ground wave proper). The receiving aerial thus responds to both waves as shown in Figure 3.9. The angle of reflection from the ground is a function of the height of the transmitting aerial. Happily, the two components of the space wave do not cancel out totally, but the strength of the space wave does increase substantially linearly with height of the receiving aerial to the maximum component of the beam, thereafter falling with further height increase.

The net effect of the two waves is that the signal field of the space wave falls inversely with the square of the distance $(1/d^2)$ from the transmitting aerial. Complete cancellation does not occur because the ground-reflected wave has a longer path than the direct wave, but the ground-reflected wave does have a destructive influence on the space wave because it undergoes a reversal of phase. This is responsible for the $1/d^2$ law. Separately the direct wave and ground-reflected wave suffer less attenuation while travelling through space other than that caused by spreading, so the signal field of each is inversely proportional to the distance $(1/d)$.

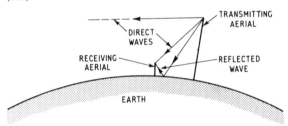

Figure 3.9. The Earth-reflected wave may detract from the direct wave at sites close to a transmitting aerial (see text)

We have seen, then, that the reception distance of v.h.f. and u.h.f. transmissions is governed by the radio-horizon distance, which is a little in advance of the optical horizon or line-of-sight distance. For country-wide coverage, a whole network of transmitters is required, which is why a multiplicity of stations are used in the UK, for example, for television and v.h.f. f.m. programmes.

Assuming a nominal tropospheric refractive index, normal v.h.f. coverage is around 100 kilometres (60 miles) from a main transmitter (less from low-power booster and relay stations), though this can be modified by the directivity of the transmitting aerial. The coverage is a little less at u.h.f.; both, however, depend on the topography and the height and gain of the receiving aerial.

Freak reception

At greater distances, the reception becomes more influenced by tropospheric refraction and diffraction of the waves round the curved Earth (Figure 3.7), and is thus less reliable. During a cyclonic weather phase, the refractive index of the troposphere may change in a way that encourages v.h.f. and u.h.f. propagation over greater-than-normal distances. However, owing to variation of the index, bad fading at relatively distant sites is often experienced at that time.

There is also a condition known as *tropospheric radio ducting* which enhances v.h.f. and u.h.f. propagation. A 'duct' consists of a stratum of the troposphere within which an abnormally large proportion of v.h.f. (or sometimes u.h.f.) signal energy is confined, and over part of all of which there exists a negative gradient of modified refractive index, bounded on its upper side by the level where the gradient becomes zero.

Freak v.h.f. and u.h.f. reception of this kind tends to occur more at the termination of a high-pressure spell, just at the time when the barometer indicates the start of a fall in pressure. Reception over several hundreds of miles is not uncommon during such periods. Radio amateurs working on 2 m (144 MHz) and the higher cm bands are very enthusiastic at those times because it allows them to communicate over distances not normally possible during 'steady-state' tropospheric conditions. If you are interested in listening on the 2 m, 70 cm and 23 cm amateur bands, you will be surprised by the distant stations you will log during a so-called 'tropo lift'.

Sporadic E

Although v.h.f. and u.h.f. waves penetrate the ionosphere, as already noted, there are times when abnormally intense ionisation occurs within the E region. A *sporadic E* layer then resolves. V.H.F. waves have greater difficulty in penetrating this layer, and some of them are reflected back to Earth at remarkably great distances from the transmitter. There are records in the archives of the BBC's v.h.f. signals having been picked up as far afield as South Africa, This, of course, is abnormal or *freak* v.h.f. reception.

Radio amateurs working on the v.h.f. and, perhaps, higher-frequency bands are also on the lookout for signs of sporadic E (E_s) propagation since this again allows them to operate over longer distances than normal. E_s starts mainly around the spring time and continues (albeit intermittently) during the summer months. Sometimes E_s and tropo propagation work together, and both effects have been detected on the 11 m CB band. E_s sometimes affects even higher-frequency signals, but communication distance above v.h.f. is essentially a function of the troposphere.

However, as we have seen, more reliable long-distance communication uses the lower frequencies and relies on the sky wave and the ionosphere for propagation.

Signal reception

Energy from a signal field is extracted by means of a receiving aerial for application to a radio receiver. Radio aerials fall into three main categories – untuned, tuned and ferrite rod, illustrated in Figure 3.10.

All aerials have a natural frequency, but the type shown at (a) is not tuned specifically to the frequency of the signal being received. It is a typical 'long-wire' aerial, popular four or five decades ago, particularly in the days of the crystal set. In those days, the longer the aerial, the greater the signal strength obtained an important requirement for zero-amplification crystal sets. The aerial is still used, though possibly in less elaborate guise, by enthusiasts for receiving weak signals in the long, medium and short wavebands.

Another type of essentially untuned aerial is that used for a.m. reception in motor cars. Sometimes, however, attempts

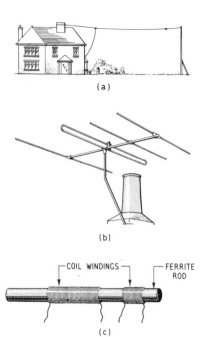

Figure 3.10. Types of receiving aerial: (a) 'untuned' long-wire; (b) tuned f.m. (v.h.f.) aerial with dipole, reflector and two directors; (c) ferrite-rod aerial

are made to tune this kind of aerial by a 'loading coil' at the bottom end, in series with the aerial and the aerial input of the receiver.

Ferrite-rod aerial

The ferrite-rod aerial is found in transistor radios and some hi-fi receivers for a.m. reception. In most cases, this sort of aerial carries the long- and medium-wave aerial coils, which are resonated to the required frequency by the receiver's aerial tuning capacitor (tuning is explained in Chapter 5).

The ferrite-rod aerial is a development of the early 'frame aerial'. The coils are wound on a core of ferrite material, which has a very high permeability to signals in the long and medium wavebands. This means that the ferrite rod has a great 'attraction' for the magnetic field of a radio wave. The magnetic component is thus concentrated along the ferrite rod and through the coils, as shown in Figure 3.11, but only when the rod is orientated to line up with the magnetic component of the radio wave. This makes the aerial most

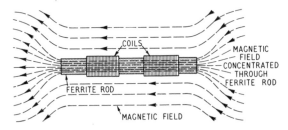

Figure 3.11. Ferrite-rod aerial principle. The high permeability of the ferrite rod concentrates the magnetic component of the radio wave through the coils wound on the rod. The coils, generally corresponding to the long- and medium-wave aerial coils, are usually tuned by a variable capacitor

responsive to signals arriving broadside to the rod, and least responsive to signals arriving end-on. The ferrite-rod aerial is thus directional, and has a figure-of-eight polar diagram, showing maximum sensitivity at the sides and minimum sensitivity at the ends. This is rather like the polar diagram of a dipole aerial when responding to horizontally polarised signals (see Figure 3.13(a)).

Tuned aerials

Tuned aerials are used mostly for the reception of f.m. broadcasts in Band 2 (a part of the v.h.f. band), as well as for television reception in the v.h.f. and u.h.f. bands. One distinction between tuned and untuned aerials, such as the 'long-wire' aerial mentioned above, is that the overall length of the former is equal, at least, to a half-wavelength of the signal (note that, with a quarter-wave aerial, the missing quarter wave is 'reflected' by the Earth, sheet of metal, wire gauze, etc.), while the length of the latter is generally only a small fraction of the signal half-wavelength.

This reveals the dometic impracticability of a tuned aerial for the long or medium waveband. For example, an aerial of about 750 m would be needed to tune the BBC's Radio 2 programme on the long waveband!

The length becomes quite manageable on the v.h.f. and u.h.f. bands. At 3 m wavelength (corresponding to 100 MHz at the top of the f.m. band), a tuned aerial is only 1.5 m in length. On the short wavebands, too, pole-mounted tuned aerials are often used by enthusiasts and commercial-radio receiving (and transmitting!) stations.

When an aerial is tuned, it becomes possible to make it directional and thus have a greater gain in a particular direction (or directions) relative to the gain of a simple omnidirectional aerial.

Figure 3.12 shows at (a) a complete wave of radio signal and a conductor of a length that just 'fits' into one half-wavelength of the signal. A conductor of such a length is described as a *half-wave aerial*. In reality, the length of the conductor is around 5 per cent shorter than the free-field signal wavelength, when it is tuned to half-wavelengths, because the wave velocity is slightly reduced from its free-field velocity when being received by an aerial. The *propagation velocity*, as it is called, of a tuned aerial depends on its length/diameter ratio.

The signal field induces current and voltage components into the aerial, the current being at a maximum and the voltage at a minimum at the centre of the half-wave aerial when it is correctly tuned, as shown in Figure 3.12(b).

It is possible to obtain a coupling from (or to) the aerial at high current and low voltage (and hence at low impedance) at the centre, or at low current and high voltage (and hence at high impedance) at one end. The usual method is to couple at low impedance at the centre, as shown in Figure 3.12(c). This is facilitated merely by breaking the half-wave aerial at the centre point and connecting the feeder or download

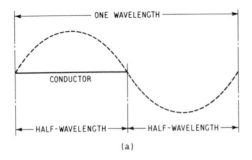

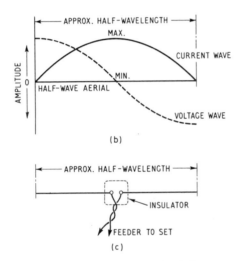

Figure 3.12. The development of a half-wave dipole; (a) shows a conductor corresponding to a signal half-wavelength, (b) the resulting current and voltage distribution and (c) the connections at the centre of the aerial for coupling it to the receiver (or transmitter)

across the resulting small gap. Since the impedance at this point is around 75 ohms, coaxial cable with a characteristic impedance of similar value is commonly used as the downlead, or *feeder* as it is called.

Matching

For maximum energy transfer from the aerial to the receiver (or from the transmitter to the aerial), the impedance of the feeder needs to correspond to that of the aerial's feed point, and the receiver's aerial input (or transmitter's feed to the aerial) needs to correspond to the impedance of the feeder. This is called *matching*.

When a tuned aerial is end-fed, it is necessary to use a matching device to translate the high end-impedance to the value corresponding to the impedance of the feeder. Matching may also be required at the receiver, to match the feeder impedance to the impedance of the aerial input circuit. From the radio reception point of view this is significant when it is required to couple an aerial using 75-ohm coaxial feeder to an f.m. receiver or tuner with 300 ohms aerial input impedance.

Coaxial feeder by its nature is so-called 'unbalanced'. The aerial input circuit of an f.m. receiver or tuner, when 300 ohms (or 240 ohms, the European 'standard'), is balanced, Thus the matching device must also change the unbalanced coaxial to a balanced receiver coupling. A 'balun' (short for balanced-to-unbalanced, or vice versa) transformer is commonly used for this.

It is possible, of course, to obtain a 240- or 300-ohm coupling from a tuned aerial. A corresponding balanced feeder can then be used to couple the aerial direct to the balanced input of the f.m. receiver or tuner. However, in the UK coaxial cable of about 75 ohms impedance is commonly used both for television and radio reception.

Amateur radio people commonly use an antenna 'tuner' (really an impedance matcher) to couple and match antennae to their transmitters and receivers.

Polarisation

The plane of polarisation of the radio wave determines the mounting of the aerial for maximum response. As already noted, a wave is said to be horizontally polarised when its lines of electric field are horizontal at the wave front, and vertically polarised when its lines of electric field are vertical.

For maximum response of a vertically-polarised wave the aerial needs to be vertically disposed, and horizontally disposed when the wave polarisation is horizontal. F.M. signals in the Band 2 part of the v.h.f. spectrum are essentially horizontally polarised (some stations are also using so-called 'slant polarisation', which yields a compromise response to vertically mounted car f.m. aerials, for example, and ordinary domestic f.m. aerials mounted horizontally; see Chapter 4); that is why f.m. aerials are mounted so that their elements are horizontal to the ground. Vertical or horizontal polarisation is used by television stations, the idea being to provide greater discrimination between signals from different transmitters sharing a common channel (frequency).

Directionality

A simple dipole, mounted vertically, responds more or less equally to signals arriving from all directions, as shown in Figure 3.13(b). When mounted horizontally, however, for the reception of horizontally polarised signals, its polar diagram is rather like a figure-of-eight, as shown in Figure 3.13(a). This

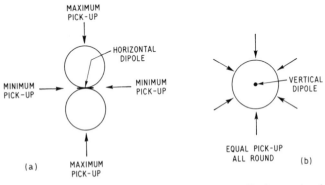

Figure 3.13. Polar diagrams for dipole; (a) horizontally disposed and (b) vertically disposed

implies that maximum signal pick-up occurs when the aerial is broadside on to the arriving signal, and that least pick-up occurs when either end of the aerial is pointing to the transmitter.

Multi-element aerials

To provide maximum discrimination against unwanted signals, v.h.f. and u.h.f. aerials are often designed specifically to be directional, so that maximum pick-up occurs with the aerial lined up to the required transmitter, while the response falls off to signals arriving from other directions. This technique also improves the gain of the aerial over that of a simple dipole in its direction of maximum response.

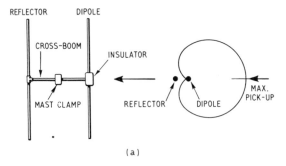

(a)

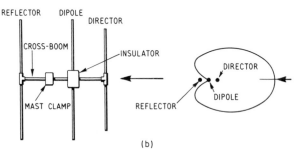

(b)

Figure 3.14. Tuned arrays; (a) two-element 'H' type and (b) three-element; with approximate polar diagrams

69

Directivity is provided in both planes of polarisation by placing 'parasitic' elements in parallel with the dipole. An element behind the dipole relative to the direction of the required signal is called a *reflector*, while an element in front is called a *director*. The term 'parasitic' is applicable because the reflector and director do not necessarily need to be connected *electrically* to the dipole. Aerials of this kind designed for f.m. and television reception usually have a single reflector (though several elements may be used to form this) and one, two or more directors, depending on the directionality pattern and gain requirements. An aerial comprising a dipole, reflector and one director is known as a three-element array; a four-element array would thus consist of reflector, dipole and two directors. A two-element ('H' type aerial) consists of the dipole plus reflector *or* one director.

Such an aerial (two-element array) is shown in Figure 3.14(a), along with its approximate polar diagram, while a three-element array (with the addition of a director) is shown at (b), also with its polar diagram. In general, there is an improvement in gain and directionality with increasing number of elements; but beyond a certain number the rate of improvement diminishes, it then being better to couple together one or more *pairs* of arrays in stacked or broadside formation.

Folded dipole

When parasitic elements are added to a simple dipole its centre impedance tends to fall from its intrinsic 75 ohms. So that matching to 'standard' 75 ohms coaxial feeder can still be achieved, the dipole is often folded, as shown in Figure 3.15. A single fold like this increases the impedance fourfold while increasing bandwidth. Thus, if the impedance of a non-folded dipole falls to, say, 18 ohms owing to the presence of parasitics, the fold restores the coupling impedance to about 72 ohms.

A reflector is approximately 5 per cent longer than the dipole, and the first director about 5 per cent shorter than the

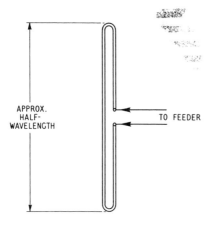

Figure 3.15. Simple folded dipole, which gives a feeder coupling impedance four times that of a non-folded dipole

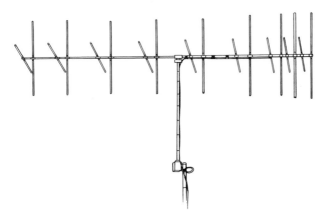

Figure 3.16. 2-metre beam aerial of both vertical and horizontal polarisation (separate feeders for each section) with 2 × 9 elements including the dipoles used for amateur radio work by the author. This is mounted on a rotator operated by a direction-indicating control box in the radio shack

71

dipole; subsequent directors may remain the same length, or their lengths may be progressively reduced, depending on the requirements and overall design.

Radio amateurs also use multi-element 'beam' aerials for transmitting and receiving. Figure 3.16 shows the author's 2 m amateur aerial which has nine elements (including the dipole) in both vertical and horizontal planes (giving the cross effect). Each section has its own run of feeder cable allowing the polarisation to be switched as required at the

Table 3.1. Broadcasting bands

Long waves	150–285 kHz
Medium waves	525–1605 kHz
120 metre band	2.300–2.495 MHz
90 "	3.200–3.400 MHz
75 "	3.900–4.000 MHz
60 "	4.750–5.060 MHz
49 "	5.950–6.200 MHz
41 "	7.100–7.300 MHz
31 "	9.500–9.775 MHz
25 "	11.700–11.975 MHz
19 "	15.100–15.450 MHz
16 "	17.700–17.900 MHz
13 "	21.450–21.750 MHz
11 "	25.600–26.100 MHz

Table 3.2. Amateur bands

160 metre band ('top band')	1.81 – 2.00 MHz
80 metre band	3.50–4.00 MHz*
40 "	7.00–7.30 MHz**
30 "	10.10–10.15 MHz
20 "	14.00–14.35 MHz
15 "	21.00–21.45 MHz
10 "	28.00–29.70 MHz
4 "	70.025–70.50 MHz***
2 "	144.00–148.00 MHz****

*   U.K. allocation 3.50 – 3.8 MHz
**   U.K. allocation 7.00–7.10 MHz
*** U.K.
**** U.K. allocation 144.00 – 146.00 MHz

transceiver (2 m rig!). The array is mounted on a rotator whose electric motor can be operated from a direction-indicating control box in the radio shack.

Like the dipole, the parasitic elements also respond to the radio wave; but instead of delivering signal to the feeder they re-radiate and hence reinforce the dipole signal when the array is aligned to the station.

There are various other configurations of tuned aerials, and readers requiring more practical information on design, performance, etc. may find useful the author's *The Practical Aerial Handbook*, 2nd edition (Newnes Technical Books).

Figure 3.17 gives the basic v.h.f. coverage, while Table 3.1 defines the broadcast bands and Table 3.2 some of the amateur bands. Additional bands above 146 MHz are also permitted for amateur use, including 430–432 MHz, 432–440 MHz and higher frequencies still up to 24.25 GHz. Various stipulations apply to the use of these and other amateur bands, details of which can be obtained from *Beginner's Guide to Amateur Radio* (Newnes Technical Books).

CB aerials

By law a 27 MHz CB aerial must not exceed 1.5 m in length. This excludes the length of the loading coil located at the bottom of the aerial. The aerial is effectively a shortened quarter-wave resonator which is completed by a ground plane configuration of some sort. Now, a truly resonant quarter-wave aerial at 27 MHz would need to be about 2.64 m in length, taking account of the velocity factor of the conductor (e.g. $300 \times 0.95/27 \times 4$). It is seen, therefore, that a legal 27 MHz CB aerial falls short of this by around 43 per cent. Thus to get the aerial to resonate, to improve its transmission characteristics and to secure a suitable match to 50-ohm coaxial feeder, it must contain a loading coil, and to satisfy the Home Office requirements this must be located at the bottom of the aerial so that it appears in series with the aerial and the inner conductor of the coaxial feeder. The

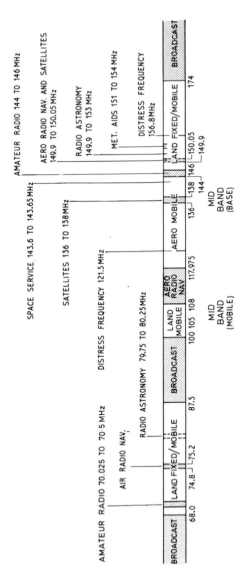

Figure 3.17. Use of v.h.f. bands

outer conductor or braid of the feeder is then connected to the ground plane.

With a mobile station, the ground plane is normally the metal body of the motor car on which the aerial is mounted, and although there may not be a direct d.c. connection here, there will be an r.f. connection owing to the coupling capacitance between the braid-connected aerial base and the metal of the car.

With a home-base station the ground plane can be a sheet of metal, a sheet of wire netting or wires or rods horizontal, drooping or downward sloping. In fact, the Home Office intimate that any kind of ground plane can be used – its arrangement and size left to individual preference.

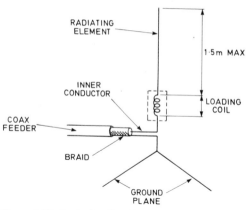

Figure 3.18. Basic details of legal 27 MHz CB aerial

The basic set-up of a ground plane aerial is shown in Figure 3.18. Without a loading coil the terminating impedance would be capacitive owing to the aerial being shorter than resonance. The loading coil balances out this capacitance by inductance thereby leaving an essentially resistive terminating impedance fairly close to the 50 ohms required by the feeder and hence the CB rig. In practice the impedance is optimised by adjusting the length of the radiating element slightly (or, perhaps, the ground-plane element(s)) until the best standing wave ratio (s.w.r.) is indicated on transmit. For this, of course, an s.w.r. meter needs to be connected between the feeder and the aerial input of the rig. These are now readily available to the CB enthusiast and some include a

Figure 3.19. SWR and power meter of Italian design distributed by Telecomms of Portsmouth

power meter, as that shown in Figure 3.19, so that you can tell how much power the transmitter is delivering. You should aim for an s.w.r. not much more than 1.5:1.

SWR adjustments

A too-high s.w.r., meaning that the aerial is failing to match the transmitter correctly, can damage the power stage of the transmitter. The aim should be to secure the best (lowest) s.w.r. over the 40 channels of 27 MHz CB. If the s.w.r. is low on channel 1 and high on channel 40, this is an indication that the aerial requires shortening slightly. Conversely, a high s.w.r. on channel 1 and a lower one on channel 40 should lead you to try increasing the length of the aerial slightly. An optimised system would give a very low s.w.r. on channel 20 with a slight rise changing down to channel 1 and up to channel 40; but this ideal state is very difficult to achieve in practice. A 1:1 s.w.r. cannot be obtained over the entire band and it is pointless in trying to get the s.w.r. much below 1.5:1 – the power loss at this ratio is but a mere 4 per cent anyway.

With an efficient loading coil and ground plane the effective radiated power (e.r.p.) from the legally-allowed 4 W of r.f. output from the transmitter need not be less than around 2 W; but can be considerably less than this with poor aerial and ground-plane systems. The Home Office would not expect the loading coil to have a length exceeding about 100 mm or a diameter exceeding about 50 mm. Including the outer housing, the overall length of the coil assembly should not be more than about 150 mm. The loading coil should not itself radiate; indeed, to do so would indicate poor efficiency. A coil arranged so as to radiate deliberately would fail to meet the terms of the CB licence.

When the aerial is mounted higher above ground than 7 m the transmitter power has to be dropped by 10 dB (to 0.4 W) to satisfy the licence conditions. This is because, as we have already seen, an aerial becomes increasingly more effective as its height is increased and hence the potential for causing interference to other services is also increased. Moreover, the stipulated base loading coil acts as a low-pass filter (l.p.f.), thereby reducing the level of harmonics radiated by the aerial.

CB interference

In some cases interference might still be experienced on TV sets in close proximity to a CB station. This can be reduced by keeping the CB aerial as far as possible away from the TV aerial and keeping the CB aerial behind the TV aerial so that it is pointing away from the CB aerial. It is sometimes impossible to operate with an indoor CB aerial owing to TVI (television interference) problems, and the trouble can be aggravated by CB aerial mismatch (excessive s.w.r.) and by the use of certain types of r.f.-switched aerial preamplifiers in the CB aerial feeder (this is different, of course, from the use of an illegal power amplifier for transmit, sometimes called a linear amplifier or 'burner'). A range of filters which can be connected in series with the feeder of an affected TV receiver are marketed by Telecomms of Portsmouth under the AKD (Blackline Series) banner.

Such a filter is shown in Figure 3.20, which is a high-pass filter (h.p.f.) including a braid-breaker. Evaluation in the

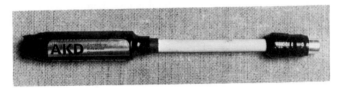

Figure 3.20. High-pass filter with braid breaker (the latter to defeat braid-induced r.f.) used by the author to minimise amateur and CB interference from TV. This and other filters of similar styling are marketed by Telecomms of Portsmouth

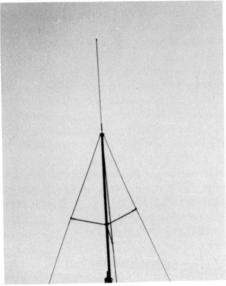

Figure 3.21. The Thunderpole 27 MHz CB aerial which has been evaluated in the author's lab. It is pictured at the test site

author's lab has proved that the filter is effective in removing certain types of TVI caused not only by CB but also amateur radio and other unwanted transmissions.

With 934 MHz CB it is possible to use properly resonant dipole and beam aerials with gain. These are of the same basic design as those described for f.m. radio earlier in this chapter. Whereas a base-loaded 1.5 m single element is permitted on 27 MHz, the licencing conditions allow for up to four elements on 934 MHz (also see Chapter 11). This implies a gain of around 5 dB and an e.r.p. up to 25 W maximum in the beam direction from the allowed-for r.f. power at u.h.f.

A home-base 27 MHz ground-plane CB aerial evaluated by the author is shown in Figure 3.21 located at the test site. This aerial, known as the Thunderpole, was found to be an efficient performer.

4

Transmitter principles

A radio transmitter consists of a carrier-wave generator and a modulator (Figure 4.1). The carrier wave needs to have its frequency controlled very accurately, which is achieved at relatively low power, while the high power required to couple to the transmitting aerial is obtained by power amplification.

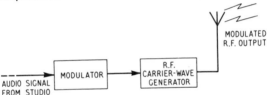

Figure 4.1. A radio transmitter consists of a carrier-wave generator and modulator, the former feeding signal energy to the aerial and the latter receiving programme signal

The front end of a transmitter therefore consists of a low power generator of radio-frequency (r.f.) signal. This is called the *master oscillator*. Valves and/or transistors are used in this section, and the frequency of the signal is held within very tight limits by means of a resonating device or circuit of some kind.

A simple and well known resonator is the tuning fork, which vibrates at a fairly constant audio frequency as governed by the mechanical properties of compliance (the reciprocal of stiffness) and mass. This low frequency could be multiplied many times electronically to produce an r.f. output. This is not necessary, however, because there are different resonators that operate at much higher frequencies; at r.f., in fact. One of these is quartz crystal, and this is commonly used for transmitter frequency control. Such a crystal (there are others such as treated or 'polarised' ceramic and barium titanate) changes dimensionally when an electric field is applied to it; conversely, it yields an electric field when subjected to mechanical stress or bending. This is called the *piezoelectric effect*, the crystals being known as *piezoelectric crystals*.

Another electronic resonator consists of an inductor and capacitor connected in parallel. More information is given on these components in Chapters 5 and 6; but at this juncture it is noteworthy that the mechanical analogue of capacitance is *compliance* and that of inductance is *mass*. Thus, just as a resonance (natural vibration) effect is achieved mechanically by mass and compliance, so the effect is achieved electronically (but at a higher frequency) by inductance and capacitance. The resonance frequency (f_o) is equal to $1/2\pi\sqrt{(LC)}$, where L is inductance (or mass) and C is capacitance (or compliance).

Electronic resonance results from electrons flowing out of the inductance to charge the capacitance, and then out of the capacitance into the inductance (see also Chapter 5). The oscillatory cycle is sustained by a transistor, integrated circuit, other solid-state device or thermionic valve in a feedback circuit. The frequency stability of the ordinary LC tuned circuit, however, is not sufficiently good for transmission purposes, hence the use of a piezoelectric crystal. The resonance frequency of a crystal is inversely proportional to its thickness. For very high frequencies the crystal frequency may be multiplied electronically to avoid the use of a very thin crystal. Moreover, certain cuts of crystal result in strong overtones, one of which may be selected for very-high-frequency operation. Improved frequency stability is achieved by maintaining the temperature of the crystal constant, and crystal ovens are used in broadcast transmitters for this purpose.

Frequency synthesisation

Another scheme which provides easy step-change in frequency is called *frequency synthesisation*. Frequency of transmission is still controlled by a quartz crystal oscillator but instead of being used directly the frequency is divided, as is also the frequency from a separate voltage-controlled oscillator (v.c.o.). The two divided signals are then applied to a phase-detector. This yields a d.c. output when the frequencies and their phase are non-coincident. The d.c. is filtered to clear it of r.f. ripple and is fed to the controlling input of the v.c.o.

It then becomes possible to change the v.c.o. frequency, and hence the transmission frequency, in small steps related to the divide ratio involved. Heart of the scheme is the phase-lock loop which is formed by the phase-detector and v.c.o. The d.c. fed to the v.c.o. pulls it onto the correct frequency and locks it to the crystal reference. The locking occurs in a very narrow bandwidth, tantamount to a high-Q circuit, and it is then only on the precise pre-arranged steps that a synthesised signal output occurs. The technique is adopted in many items of latest radio equipment, including receivers for the synthesisation of the local oscillator frequency and amateur radio and CB transceivers. The technique also makes it possible to read-out the precise frequency of transmission and reception digitally to a very high degree of accuracy. On some 2 m transceivers the synthesised steps can be switched right down to 100 Hz, which is rather remarkable when related to 144 MHz! More details of the arrangement and circuitry involved are given in Chapter 11. Phase-lock loop integrated circuits (i.cs.) make the technique much less complex to handle than hitherto.

The signal from the master oscillator is commonly applied to a *buffer amplifier* before being applied to the *power amplifier*, and automatic gain control (a.g.c.) may be used to stabilise the amplitude of the signal, as shown in Figure 4.2.

The stages used in the audio section are shown in Figure 4.3. The first amplifiers boost the low-level signals from the programme lines, the next stage prevents the amplitude of the signals from rising to a level that would over-modulate the transmitter.

The modulator-driver and power-amplifier stages build up the modulation signal to the power required to modulate the carrier wave. Overall design is towards low distortion,

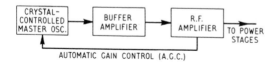

Figure 4.2. Block schematic of the pre-stages of the r.f. carrier-wave generator, showing the crystal-controlled oscillator stage and a.g.c. for amplitude control

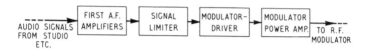

Figure 4.3. The modulator stages of an a.m. transmitter

especially in the f.m. system, and control circuits and equipment are used extensively at the front end of the audio channel. Signal from the studio centre is often fed to the modulator input circuits through radio links or landlines.

Amplification classes and efficiency

Efficiency of r.f. amplification is related to the class in which the power amplifier stage is operated. There are three primary classes which are A, B and C. A valve or transistor operating in class A passes output current (from anode or collector) over the full signal cycle. On the other hand, class B and C amplifiers pass output current only during a part of the signal cycle, class C for a smaller part of the signal cycle than class B. Amplification is thus 'linear' at class A but non-linear at class B and C. However, in audio amplifiers it is possible to secure linear operation by using class B push-pull operation; that is, by using one valve or transistor to handle the positive-going half of the signal cycle and the other to handle the negative-going half. Suitable circuit design then makes it possible to fit the two halves together so that the output consists of a relatively undistorted yet amplified replica of the input.

When we are dealing with r.f. signal, however, it is possible to use class C amplification. This is because the r.f. signal drives into a 'tank' tuned circuit at the output and all that is required to sustain oscillation of this are 'synchronised' bursts of output which, of course, are just what a class C amplifier delivers. The 'flywheel' effect of the tuned output circuit produces a 'clean', full-cycle r.f. output.

This is provided the r.f. signal is not modulated by audio such that its amplitude is caused to vary. This means, then, that with single sideband (s.s.b.) modulation a *linear* r.f. power amplifier must be used. The same applies to amplitude modulation but only when the r.f. has undergone modulation prior to its application to the r.f. power amplifier. This would be the case when so-called 'low-level' amplitude modulation is used or when it is required further to boost the output of an a.m. transmitter by an additional power amplifier. In those cases class C. r.f. power amplification cannot be used, so class AB or, perhaps, B amplification is used instead, leading to somewhat lower efficiency. Class AB implies that the stage is operated somewhere between class A and B.

For high-level a.m. the r.f. power amplifier can be operated in class C because this time the modulation is effectively 'added' to the r.f. signal actually in the r.f. power amplifier itself. This is achieved by a fairly high-power modulator stage. As an example, a 200 W transmitter would require a modulation stage capable of producing some 100 W of clean audio for full amplitude modulation. With low-level modulation the audio power requirement is considerably less than this but the shortfall is that the r.f. power amplifier cannot then be operated in the more efficient class C mode.

The audio frequency (a.f.) stages comprising the modulator (commonly push-pull class B in large transmitters using high-level modulation) must, of course, employ linear amplification to retain a low level of audio distortion, so class A, AB and push-pull B stages are found here.

Because the amplitude of the r.f. with frequency modulation (f.m.) remains constant it is possible to employ a class C r.f. power amplifier without evoking serious distortion.

Greatest conversion efficiency occurs with class C owing to the smaller mean anode or collector current involved. Class A is the least efficient, but in low-level audio circuits this is of little moment. Class AB might be adopted to improve the efficiency marginally without producing excessive non-linear distortion. It is, of course, essential to avoid over-modulation, especially with a.m. or s.s.b., since this itself evokes very serious distortion and causes the signal to spread out beyond its normally-allocated spectrum space, thereby inciting bad splatter or 'spitch' interference on adjacent frequencies which might be occupied by other stations.

F.M. transmitter

A number of schemes for frequency-modulating a v.h.f. carrier wave have evolved over the years, and a development of an original arrangement pioneered by the late E. A. Armstrong, of f.m. radio fame, is given by the block diagram in Figure 4.4.

Here audio signals are passed through a.f. amplifiers and pre-emphasis circuits, the latter giving a progressive boost to the higher audio frequencies (see page 87), and thence to a special modulator, which also receives phased-signal from the crystal oscillator, via the buffer amplifier. The frequency of the signal produced by the crystal oscillator stage is related to the v.h.f signal fed to the aerial, but is much lower than this. The amount by which the r.f. signal is fully deviated by the peak audio signal at the modulator also has a relationship to the final deviation which, for high quality radio broadcasting, is ±75 kHz (see Chapter 2).

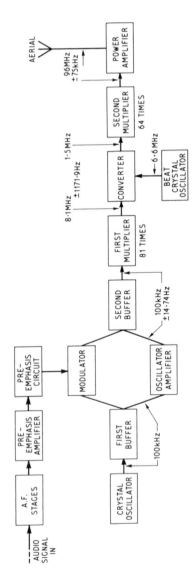

Figure 4.4. Block diagram of f.m. transmitter – see text

86

Now, lets us suppose that a transmitter with this maximum deviation is required to operate at a nominal carrier frequency of 96 MHz. As shown in Figure 4.4, this can be obtained by starting with a 100 kHz oscillator frequency and engineering for the modulator to deviate this by ±14.74 Hz. This signal is then passed, via the second buffer, to the first multiplier, which increases the frequency 81 times to 8.1 MHz and the deviation to ±1171.9 Hz. The signal at that frequency and deviation is then applied to the converter stage, along with a signal of 6.6 MHz from the beat crystal oscillator, and the beat or heterodyne signal at 1.5 MHz ($8.1 - 6.6 = 1.5$) is filtered out. The deviation of this signal remains at ±1171.9 Hz because there is neither frequency multiplication nor division, just conversion.

The second multiplier increases the frequency of the signal and its deviation by 64 times, which thus yields a signal of the nominal 96 MHz carrier frequency and ±75 kHz deviation. R.F. amplification also occurs in the multipliers, and a final lift of power is provided by the power-amplifier stage feeding the aerial system.

Pre- and de-emphasis

A primary attribute of the f.m. system of broadcasting is its significantly greater signal-to-noise ratio and hence programme dynamic range compared with the a.m. system. Most noise (and by noise is meant the background 'sizzle' and 'hiss' that becomes more and more noticeable as the fidelity of sound reproduction is enhanced) occurs towards the treble end of the audio spectrum. On the f.m. system it is possible to boost the treble frequencies of the modulation signal during transmission, and to attenuate them correspondingly at the receiver to restore frequency balance. This technique is called *pre-emphasis* as it applies to the transmitter and *de-emphasis* as it applies to the receiver. The pre-emphasis does not affect the receiver noise, but the de-emphasis reduces the noise at the receiver while restoring the frequency balance.

The rate of pre- and de-emphasis is expressed as a time-constant, which is 50 μs in the UK, Europe, Australia, etc. and 75 μs in the US. Also in the US the Dolby noise-reducing artifice (see the author's *The Audio Handbook*) is sometimes used with the f.m. system of broadcasting, and to fit in better with this the time-constant is reduced to 25 μs.

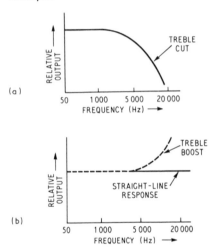

Figure 4.5. Improved signal-to-noise performance is achieved on the f.m. system by pre-emphasis at the transmitter and de-emphasis at the receiver; (a) shows the nature of the de-emphasis response characteristic, and (b) the 'flat' overall response eventually obtained due to the transmitter pre-emphasis, shown by broken line

Figure 4.5 shows at (a) the de-emphasis applied at the receiver (or f.m. tuner), and at (b) how the frequency response is restored when corresponding pre-emphasis is applied at the transmitter. See also Chapters 5 and 10.

Some of the BBC f.m. transmitters are equipped with variable de-emphasis limiters, which automatically and momentarily reduce the pre-emphasis when there is large-amplitude, high-frequency content in the modulation signal. This avoids transmitter over-modulation on high frequencies without the need for peak clipping.

Narrow-band FM

Although broadcast entertainment f.m. stations use a deviation of ±75 kHz, stations used solely for communications employ a deviation much less than this to keep the spread of the signal within a small band-width. This is called 'narrow-band f.m.' (n.b.f.m.) and although the quality of reproduction is nowhere near as high as that possible with wide deviation it is, nevertheless, adequate for communications purposes. It is, in fact, superior to the quality of most s.s.b. transmissions and has the advantage over basic a.m. owing to the capture effect, though this is not as potent as possible with wide-band f.m.

Deviation of n.b.f.m. amateur radio stations is around 2.5 to 3 kHz, and somewhat less than this from 27 MHz CB transceivers (see Chapter 11). Amateur radio operators using f.m. endeavour to prevent their modulation index exceeding about 0.6, the signal band-width then being similar to that of a.m. with a restriction of 2.5 to 3 kHz applied to the audio modulation.

Power output

In recent times radio amateurs have found it necessary to look at power output in terms of dB power ratios (if only to pass the RAE!). Power output allowed depends on the band used. The maximum carrier power supplied to the aerial is given now as 20 dBW, which merely means an r.f. level 20 dB above 1 W. Because a power ratio of 20 dB corresponds to a direct ratio of 100:1, 20 dBW implies an r.f. level of 100 W. It is noteworthy that this is the steady-state 'average' power of the r.f. – derived, for example, by squaring the r.f. voltage across the transmitter load and then dividing the result by the resistive value of the load, *or* by squaring the r.f. current through the load and multiplying the result by the resistive value of the load.

On f.m. that would be the steady-state power because with this mode the amplitude of the carrier remains constant. With a.m. and s.s.b. operation, things are different because the amplitude of the r.f. (carrier) is rising and falling in sympathy with the modulation. When a transmitter is fully modulated to 100 per cent (modulation factor 1), the r.f. amplitude on the peaks of the modulation is two times that of the amplitude of the unmodulated carrier wave. Thus, let's suppose that the transmitter is driving into a 50-ohm resistive load and that the r.f. across the load is 70.71 V when there's no modulation. Doing the little sum mentioned above we find that the steady-state average power then works out close to 100 W. Now let's suppose that the carrier is amplitude-modulated to 100 per cent. The r.f. voltage on the *peaks* of the modulation envelope will now be 2 × 70.71, or close to 141.42 V. Doing the sum again we now get a power output close to 400 W, which is four times the power of the unmodulated carrier wave. This is known as the peak envelope power (p.e.p.), 400 W p.e.p. being the maximum power allowed under the amateur licencing conditions. Expressed as a decibel ratio a four-times power increase is 6 dB, so the maximum p.e.p. is thus 26 dBW.

Before the days of dBW, amateurs assessed their power output in terms of d.c. input to the power amplifier while taking account of the efficiency of the stage. Power input is obtained by finding the product of the voltage applied to and the current taken by the r.f. power amplifier. For example, a valve r.f. power amplifier may draw 100 mA (0.1 A) at a voltage of 2 kV (2 000 V) so that the input power is 200 W. If the efficiency of the power amplifier is 50 per cent (factor of 0.5), then the r.f. output would approximate 100 W.

Aerial characteristics

As noted in Chapter 3, v.h.f. aerials usually have a gain factor, so that the r.f. power fed into them is stepped up to a larger effective radiated power in all directions or in specific directions (usually the latter), depending on the service area requirements. The polar diagram in Figure 4.6 shows the horizontal directionality of the IBA's v.h.f. aerial for the independent local radio station at Croydon on 97.3 MHz. It is noteworthy that the signal field contains vertically as well as horizontally polarised components to satisfy the requirements of listeners using portable transistor receivers and car radios for the f.m. programme. The maximum advantage

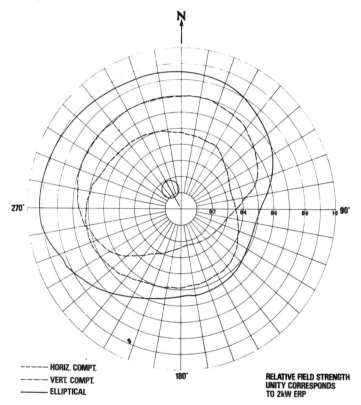

- - - - - HORIZ. COMPT.
- - - - - VERT. COMPT.
———— ELLIPTICAL

RELATIVE FIELD STRENGTH
UNITY CORRESPONDS
TO 2kW ERP

Figure 4.6. The horizontal radiation pattern of IBA's Croydon v.h.f. aerial on 97.3 MHz (courtesy Independent Broadcasting Authority)

gained from mixed polarisation varies between 6 dB for car reception and about 12 dB for rod-aerial reception at open, outdoor sites, at the expense of a little loss to normal reception on outdoor horizontally-disposed v.h.f. aerials. The mixed polarisation gives rise to so-called elliptical polarisation, the component of which is also indicated on Figure 4.6.

F.M. programme input

Two programme lines commonly arrive at a v.h.f. f.m. transmitter from the studio centre for the left and right channels of a stereo signal. As with the single-channel mono line for a medium-frequency a.m. transmitter, these are rented.

Radio links are also used at super high freqency (s.h.f.), each link carrying a multiplicity of high-quality sound signals or fewer, wider-band video signals, thereby making it relatively easy to secure balanced stero pairs of circuits.

Pulse-code-modulation linking

Of significant importance is the pulse code modulation (p.c.m.) technique, used by the BBC for the linking of studio centres and programme sources to f.m. transmitters. It is based on the digital or binary principle used in computers, and in this way differs from the more conventional 'analogue-signal linking', as it is sometimes called.

With p.c.m. the audio information is converted to a train of digits corresponding to amplitude samples of the signal. The conventional information results, of course, from the continuously varying electrical analogue of the sound-pressure variations at the microphone, for example, this then being conveyed through an essentially linear link system (though lack of perfect linearity and progressive boosting of the signals result in distortion and noise).

Another kind of transmission (mentioned in Chapter 2) is telegraphy, where the signal consists merely of a waveform with two or more (usually two) discrete values, corresponding to zero and one, that only need to be identified by the receiver to establish the original information. Morse code is an example. Amplification, linearity and noise are not detracting influences here, since the system can easily be designed to discount noise and to respond only to signal levels above noise.

The p.c.m. system, in fact, uses simple zero and one pulses, encoded to the pattern of the audio-signal analogue, for information conveyance. At the receiving end the pulses are decoded to yield the original analogue. The basic scheme of the system is expressed by the block diagram in Figure 4.7. Here the analogue sine-wave signal is fed to a 'sampler' through a low-pass filter (which passes low frequencies but not high frequencies), the analogue signal thus being sampled at a rate dictated by the sampling pulses.

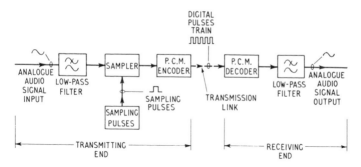

Figure 4.7. Elementary block diagram of the sending and receiving ends of a pulse-code-modulation link

The amplitude of the signal at each sampling is then encoded to correspond to a train of 'zero' and 'one' pulses, and in this form, as shown in the diagram, the signal is sent over the link. It is thus received in like form at the other end, and here the decoder restores the signal to its original analogue form, the higher-frequency residual pulses being removed by the low-pass filter.

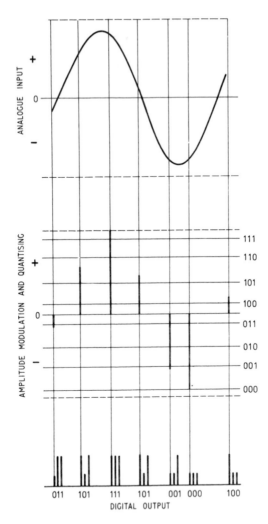

Figure 4.8. Simplified diagram showing how an analogue signal (sine wave in this example) is converted to digital format over eight quantised levels, with each level corresponding to its own three-bit word (see text)

Figure 4.8 indicates the nature of the encoding. The sine-wave analogue signal, shown at the top, swings positive and negative with respect to centre zero. This is sampled by the pulses at even intervals, so that the amplitude of the signal at each sample is conveyed to the encoder.

The encoder is arranged to produce a series of pulses of 'zero' and 'one', each series corresponding to the amplitude of the analogue. In practice, there is more to it than this, since the pulse-series so produced is related to a predetermined amplitude level, such that the amplitude of the sample has to be *nearest* to this level to evoke a corresponding pulse-series. This is called *quantising*, and the datum of the measurement can be the most positive or the most negative potential that can be assumed by the analogue signal; or zero could be made the datum.

Figure 4.8 shows eight amplitude levels, with each level corresponding to a different series of pulses. Each series is thus characteristic of one particular quantised amplitude level; in binary parlance, this is stated as each level having three 'bits per word' and each being represented by its own particular word. High-quality audio p.c.m. linking requires more than eight quantised levels, which means that each word must contain more than three bits. The number of levels is related to the number of bits n in 2^n. The BBC's system adopts thirteen bits for information, corresponding to 8192 levels, while a 'parity bit' for error correction yields an overall total of 16 384 levels.

The first bit of a word is the most signficant; in Figure 4.8, it indicates whether the excursion is positive or negative. The final bit is always the least significant.

It is clear that the analogue reconstruction at the decoder can only approximate the original signal since there will always be intervals between the sampled amplitude levels. The difference between the input and output analogues is termed 'quantising noise'; this, of course, decreases with increasing number of levels and hence with the number of bits per word.

The sampling rate needs to be at least twice the signal bandwidth. The BBC's p.c.m. audio-link system has a 32 kHz pulse repetition rate for a bandwidth of 40 Hz to 15 kHz. This gives a weighted signal-to-noise ratio of 69 dB.

The bottom part of Figure 4.8 shows the bit stream that is fed into the transmission link. The decoding is the converse of the encoding; that is, the digital input is converted to sampled amplitude levels and then to analogue signal, being finally cleared of residual sampling pulses by low-pass filtering. The link, incidentally, can be either wideband cable (i.e. coaxial cable) or microwave radio.

Stereo radio

Stereo radio requires two isolated audio links for the A and B (left and right, respectively) channels, and these are readily provided by p.c.m. Sometimes, however, the left and right signals are conveyed to the transmitter over lines rented from the transmitting authority. The programme-signal input equipment at the transmitter includes pre-emphasis for each channel and also a limiter for each channel to forestall over-modulation in the event of the sending levels or line/link losses differing from their correct values for any reason. The gain-control circuits of the limiters might also be interconnected, since under certain conditions independent gain control of the left and right channels could result in instability of the ultimate stereo image. The input equipment also includes command and supervisory logic circuitry, depending on the nature of the transmitter.

Stereo encoding involves special processing of the audio signals, as basically indicated by the block diagram in Figure 4.7. The A and B inputs pass through the pre-emphasis circuits and arrive together at a *matrix* (which is a circuit network for adding and subtracting the A and B signals), so that outputs of A + B and A − B are produced. The A + B signal is the sum of the information carried by the left and right signals, and thus corresponds to ordinary, single-channel *mono* information. The difference between the information carried by the left and right channels constitutes the *stereo* information, the A − B signal. The A + B signal is used to frequency-modulate the v.h.f. carrier wave in the usual way, which means that mono-only receivers taking signal from a stereo transmitter will respond normally to the whole of the information (i.e. that provided by both the left and right channels).

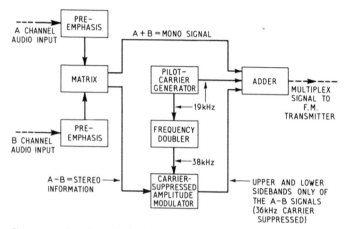

Figure 4.9. Simplied block diagram of f.m. stereo encoder (see text)

The A − B stereo information, however, is specially processed before it is added to the A + B signal. It is arranged to amplitude-modulate a 38 kHz *subcarrier* which, at the transmitter, is obtained by doubling the frequency of a 19 kHz signal produced by a crystal oscillator. The upper and lower sidebands of the A − B signal are retained, but the subcarrier itself is suppressed by the amplitude modulator, called a *balanced modulator*. The 19 kHz signal produced by the crystal oscillator is called the *pilot tone* signal. This signal, the A + B signal, and the sidebands of the A − B signal are fed to a summing amplifier whose output constitutes the *stereo multiplex signal* used to frequency-modulate the transmitter.

Figure 4.10 shows how all the components of the multiplex signal are placed in frequency relative to each other. The ordinary mono A + B signal occupies the spectrum from about 30 Hz to 15 kHz, then comes the 19 kHz pilot tone, followed by the sidebands of the A − B signal. Ordinary mono receivers bypass all the components above about 15 kHz, while receivers equipped with a stereo decoder process all the components of the multiplex signal in such a way that the receiver delivers the A and B (left and right)

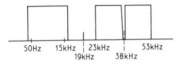

Figure 4.10. The frequencies of the components of a multiplex stereo signal

signals separately for driving separate amplifiers and loud-speakers. The action is the converse of that at the transmitter; the left output is derived by addition such that (A + B) + (A − B) = 2A, and the right output by subtraction such that (A + B) − (A − B) = 2B, remembering that A corresponds to the left channel and B to the right channel.

It is noteworthy that the level of the pilot tone along with the residual of the suppressed 38 kHz subcarrier constitutes around 10 per cent of the available modulation, leaving 90 per cent for the audio information proper. Thus, if the deviation for 100 per cent modulation is ±75 kHz, approximately ±67.5 kHz deviation is tied up with the audio information and approximately ±7.5 kHz with the pilot tone, etc. The f.m. stations of the IBA have their limiters set for a total maximum deviation of approximately 61 kHz which, in this case, corresponds to ±54.2 kHz *plus* ±6.75 kHz for the pilot tone.

A schematic diagram of the stereo encoder used by the IBA f.m. stations is given in Figure 4.11. In addition to the features already explained, this includes a provision for subsidiary channel authorisation (s.c.a.) inputs and 'command' mono/ stereo switching. The former relate to extra multiplex information carried on the common v.h.f. signal (already in use in the USA, but not in the UK), while the latter improves the

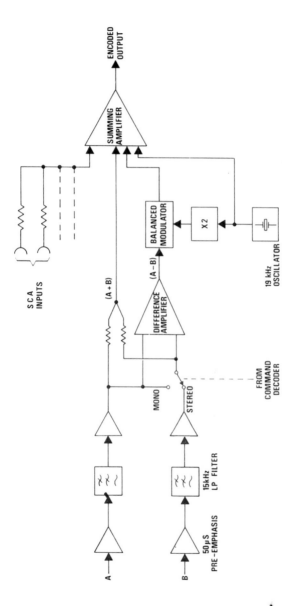

Figure 4.11. Schematic diagram of the stereo encoder used by some of the IBA f.m. stations, showing mono/stereo switching and the extra subsidiary channel authorisation (s.c.a.) inputs for possible future use (courtesy Independent Broadcasting Authority)

99

overall signal-to-noise ratio in the mono mode when long programmes in mono are being transmitted.

The decoding of the stereo multiplex signal delivered by the detector of the receiver or stereo f.m. tuner requires the accurate retrieval (in terms of frequency and phase) of the suppressed 38 kHz subcarrier. This is achieved by frequency-doubling the 19 kHz pilot tone signal, as explained in the next chapter.

5

Receiver principles

The simplest receiver consists of an aerial, earth, demodulator and headphone set, as shown by the simplified diagram in Figure 5.1. This diagram also introduces the three radio symbols for aerial, earth and headphone set. Other symbols

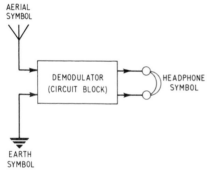

Figure 5.1. Block diagram of simplest radio receiver which, although workable, is impracticable: it would respond simultaneously to all the signals picked up by the aerial, and the headphone set would produce a jumble of sound from many stations

are introduced in this chapter and in subsequent chapters as we continue to explore radio circuits and components. Figure 5.1 is a *block diagram*, which means that a simple rectangle or some other shape is drawn to represent a circuit

101

section. This technique makes it possible to explain quite complicated operations without getting involved in the details of the circuit sections. For detailed examination of a circuit section, of course, it is necessary to show the whole circuit.

The tuned circuit

Although the receiver in Figure 5.1 is workable, the design is not at all practicable because it would respond simultaneously to all the signals picked up by the aerial. Some scheme is thus required to select the wanted signal and to reject all the unwanted ones, as shown by the 'selectivity' block in Figure 5.2. The arrow implies that something is variable, and in this case it is the frequency of the selectivity, which can be tuned over the band of interest.

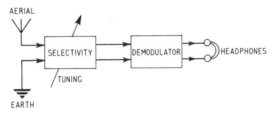

Figure 5.2. Block diagram of a more practicable circuit, where a stage of selectivity is included in front of the demodulator to accept only the wanted signal and to reject the unwanted ones. The arrow indicates variable 'selection' or tuning (see text)

Figure 5.3 shows the signals from a number of radio stations in a particular waveband, along with the curve of selectivity, which can be adjusted up and down the band. This is called the *tuning*, and a station is tuned and hence 'selected' when it is 'captured' by the selectivity curve.

Now, on opening the selectivity block the least we would find would be a coil and variable capacitor of some kind, and these two components would almost certainly be connected in parallel (one across the other). This is called a *tuned circuit* which, in Figure 5.2, is connected to the aerial and earth. The coil constitutes an *inductor* and is called the *aerial coil*, while the variable capacitor is commonly referred to as the *tuning*

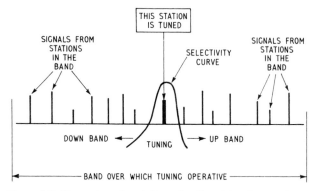

Figure 5.3. Elementary description of radio tuning (see text)

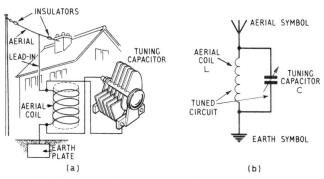

Figure 5.4. Simple parallel tuned circuit, (a) diagramatic and (b) schematic (see text)

capacitor. Figure 5.4 shows the actual components of such a tuned circuit at (a), while (b) shows the circuit and symbols of the components.

Before we can really understand how the tuned circuit works, we shall need to know a little about how an inductor and a capacitor behave when subjected to electricity. Chapter 6 shows that an inductor consists of a coil of wire and that a capacitor, in its simplest form, consists of two adjacent metal plates isolated by air or other insulator (the *dielectric*).

Thus we find that while d.c. flows through an inductor, limited by the resistance of the wire of the coil, continuous d.c. is unable to flow through a capacitor because of the insulation between the plates. However, on first switching on the supply, an ammeter connected in series with the capacitor would give a momentary reading (a 'kick' of current), which is caused by the two plates charging positively and negatively across the dielectric. If the supply is removed from a charged capacitor, and the capacitor is then connected across an ammeter, in series with a current-limiting resistor, an opposite deflection would be detected, caused by the capacitor discharging through the resistor and ammeter. A large-value capacitor is required to observe these effects.

Capacitive reactance

Now, if a.c. is fed into a capacitor, an a.c. ammeter *would* give a continuous reading owing to the capacitor charging during one half-cycle and discharging during the opposite-polarity next half-cycle. Discounting pure resistance losses, the amount of a.c. that flows through a capacitor depends on the frequency of the a.c. and on the value of the capacitance. The current flow increases with increasing frequency and capacitance, which implies that the *restriction* on the current flow decreases as the frequency and/or capacitance increases.

The restrictive effect is called *reactance*, and because it relates to a capacitor the term *capacitive reactance* is used. X is the symbol of reactance, and with a 'c' suffix indicates capacitive reactance, thus X_c. Reactance, then, is something like resistance but applicable to an a.c. circuit; a capacitor has virtually infinite resistance (depending on the insulation property of its dielectric), but a definitely finite reactance, as described by the following formula:

$$X_c = \frac{1}{2\pi fC}$$

where f is the frequency in hertz and C the capacitance in farads (see Chapter 6). This shows that the capacitive reactance is *inversely* proportional to the frequency and capacitance.

Inductive reactance

There is a similar property of reactance associated with inductors, known as inductive reactance (symbol X_L). If we measured the d.c. resistance of an inductor we would obtain a value dictated by the resistance of the wire making up the coil. The d.c. flowing, therefore, would follow the simple Ohm's Law formula of $I = V/R$.

Now, if we took this same inductor and applied an a.c. voltage, the resulting a.c. flowing would no longer be related directly to the resistance of the coil. We would find that the a.c. was less than could be accounted for by the d.c. resistance of the wire alone, depending on the frequency of the a.c. and on the value of the inductance. In this case we would discover that the inductive reactance was *directly* proportional to the frequency and inductance value, as described by the following formula:

$$X_L = 2\pi fL$$

where f is the frequency in hertz and L the inductance in henries (see Chapter 6).

The a.c. flowing through a circuit of true reactance, therefore, would be $I = V/X$, where X is either capacitive or inductive reactance.

Inductive reactance results because the rise and fall of the voltage across an inductor fails to coincide with the rise and fall of the current flowing through it. When a.c. is applied to a pure resistance, the current operates in step – or *in phase* – with the voltage. With pure inductance, however, the current *lags* the voltage by a quarter of a cycle, i.e. 90 degrees, as shown in Figure 5.5. This stems from the back e.m.f. (Chapters 1 and 6).

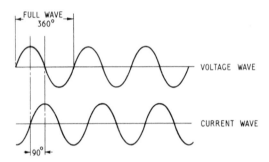

Figure 5.5. The current through a pure inductance *lags* the voltage by a quarter of a cycle (90 degrees) as shown. The opposite obtains with pure capacitance; that is, the current *leads* the voltage by a quarter of a cycle

With pure capacitance, the opposite condition obtains; that is, the current *leads* the voltage by a quarter of a cycle, or 90 degrees. This stems from the charging and discharging cycles to which a.c. subjects a capacitor. It is because of this that a *perfect* capacitor dissipates zero power (because maximum current is at zero volts and maximum voltage is at zero current).

In practice, inductance and capacitance contain components of resistance (i.e. the resistance of the coil wire and the conductors, and the resistive losses of the dielectric). Although possibly small, they modify the pure reactance, the result then being called the *impedance* (symbol Z). Like resistance, reactance and impedance are valued in terms of the ohm. Ohm's Law is also applicable, such that *I* (the a.c.) is equal to *V/Z*.

Moreover, an inductor will contain a small component of capacitance (i.e. the self-capacitance of the coil winding), while a capacitor will probably contain a small component of inductance (i.e. the effective inductance of the plates, particularly when they are formed of metal-foil strips and wound either side of a dielectric). The net value of impedance when all the components appear in series is:

$$Z = \sqrt{(R_2 + X^2)}$$

where R is the resistance and X the net impedance (which is equal to $2\pi fL - (1/2\pi fC)$). In other words, the net impedance is the algebraic sum of all the components.

Tuned-circuit principle

We can now return to the tuned circuit (Figure 5.4). It will be remembered that an increase in frequency causes the inductive reactance to rise and the capacitive reactance to fall. This means that, for any given combination of capacitance and inductance, there will be one particular frequency where the capacitive reactance will equal the inductive reactance. This is called the frequency of resonance or *resonance frequency*, where

$$\frac{1}{2\pi fC} = 2\pi fL$$

It is possible to rearrange these two reactance formulae in terms of the resonance frequency (f_0) thus:

$$f_0 = \frac{1}{2\pi\sqrt{(LC)}}$$

where L is the inductance in henries and C the capacitance in farads. As an example, if C is 200 pF and L is 200 μH, then f_0 is close to 796 kHz, which means that at f_0 $X_c = X_L$.

This is all very well, but how does a circuit such as that in Figure 5.4 select just one signal from a multiplicity picked up by the aerial? The answer is that when the capacitor is adjusted so that the circuit is *tuned* to the wanted frequency, the signal current flowing through the inductor arm is equal to that flowing through the capacitor arm (because the two are in parallel). However, because the inductor current is 180 degrees from the capacitor current (there is a 90-degee phase displacement in each arm, remember), the current in one arm is at a positive peak when the current in the other arm is at a negative peak. The result is that there is almost complete cancellation of current through the parallel combination at resonance.

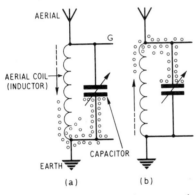

Figure 5.6. Oscillatory displacement of electrons in activated parallel-tuned circuit

In other words, at all frequencies other than the tuned or resonance frequency the aerial signals are effectively short-circuited, and only the *tuned* signal apears across the circuit. At resonance, a parallel-tuned circuit is a *rejector circuit*; that is, it has a high tuned impedance and hence low current flow.

Figure 5.6 shows what happens to the electrons in a tuned circuit. During one half-cycle of signal they flow out of the inductor to charge one plate of the capacitor as at (a), while during the other half-cycle they flow the opposite way out of the inductor to charge the other plate of the capacitor as at (b). The electron alternations result from the building up and collapsing of the changing magnetic field across the inductor. This 'oscillatory' surging to and fro of electrons continues as long as the circuit is excited by signal energy, as fed in from the aerial for example.

Figure 5.7. An oscillatory waveform whose amplitude diminishes with time is called a damped oscillation (see text)

Even when activated momentarily, the intrinsic 'flywheel' or momentum effect in the tuned circuit tends to sustain the oscillatory action for a brief period, as shown in Figure 5.7, where the amplitude of the oscillation diminishes with time at a rate depending on the circuit losses. This is called a *damped oscillation*.

Series-tuned circuit

A tuned circuit is also formed by inductance and capacitance connected in series, as shown in Figure 5.8. At resonance, the series-tuned circuit passes a relatively high signal current

Figure 5.8. Series-tuned circuit, which is sometimes called an acceptor circuit because at resonance it exhibits a low tuned impedance and hence high current flow (see text)

because the corresponding but opposing reactances of L and C cancel out; excluding losses, this results in virtually zero impedance through the circuit. At resonance, therefore, a series-tuned circuit is an *acceptor circuit*; that is, it has a low tuned impedance and hence high current flow.

109

Magnification factor

An astonishing thing about a tuned circuit lies in its ability to 'magnify' a signal. Let us assume that L and C in Figure 5.8 each have a reactance of 1000 ohms at resonance, and that the circuit and component losses result in an impedance of 20 ohms at resonance. Now, if the applied signal is, say, 100 mV the current through the circuit will be 5 mA (from Ohm's Law). This means, of course, that 5 mA must be flowing through both L and C because they are in series, so by using Ohm's Law again we find the signal voltage developed across either L or C *alone*. We have seen that the reactance at resonance of L and C is 1000 ohms, and 5 mA flowing through 1000 ohms corresponds to a p.d. of 5 V. This signal, which is present across L or C, is thus fifty times greater than the 100 mV input signal. Owing to this, such a circuit would be said to possess a *magnification* or *quality* factor (symbol Q) of 50. Q can thus be expressed as X/r, where X is the reactance and r the resistive loss in the circuit.

To summarise, then, the signal voltage across L or C of a series-tuned circuit at resonance is Q times greater than the applied signal voltage. With a parallel-tuned circuit, the current in L is very closely equal to that in C, and is Q times larger than the current in the external circuit. It will be appreciated, of course, that both L and C have their own losses (i.e. resistive losses in L and dielectric losses, etc. in C), and that these separate losses tend to modify the voltage and current conditions under resonance. Also, when a tuned circuit is connected to an external circuit (like an aerial or detector – Figure 5.2) additional losses are reflected into it.

Radio receivers adopt both series- and parallel-tuned circuits, separately and in combinations.

Plotting the voltage across or the current through a tuned circuit as the signal frequency is adjusted through resonance produces the *response curve*, an example of which for the parallel-tuned circuit is given in Figure 5.9. The width of the curve is a measure of the *selectivity*. The curve is widened, and the selectivity thus impaired, by circuit losses causing a fall in the Q factor.

The resistance of an inductor to r.f. current can be significantly higher than its resistance to d.c. As the frequency is raised so the current tends to flow closer to the surface of the wire. This so-called *skin effect* (an early radio term) is reduced by the use of silver-plated wire and conductors in equipment operating in the upper reaches of v.h.f. and beyond.

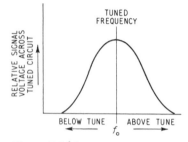

Figure 5.9. Response curve of parallel-tuned circuit: the narrower the curve, the better the selectivity

The dynamic resistance (R_d) is related to the Q-factor of the tuned circuit such that $R_d = L/Cr$ and, since $Q = 2\pi fL/r$, $R_d = Q/2\pi fC$. However, since most r.f. resistive losses occur in the inductor, it is this that is the prime determinant of the Q-factor of a tuned circuit. The capacitor has much less influence generally. A well-designed r.f. inductor will have an intrinsic Q-factor round to 100 to 400 mark, and a tuned circuit using such an inductor will have an R_d in the order of 50 000 ohms. Conversely, of course, the d.c. resistance would be very low.

It will be appreciated that a given frequency could be tuned by an infinite number of L and C values. Choice of the L/C ratio is dictated by requirements. We have seen that to obtain a high value of R_d the L/C ratio should be large; but if it is required to 'swamp' self-capacitance of a circuit as a whole, to render the tuning and/or oscillator frequency more stable, for example, a higher value C than the best for the R_d point of view might well be used. If we rely too much on stray capacitances, which may be reflected from active devices like valves and transistors, then the frequency could drift quite substantially as the devices increase in temperature. This can be reduced by making the tuned circuit C substantially greater than the stray capacitances reflected across the inductor. A good compromise for general applications has been given as 1.5 pF of C per metre of the tuned signal wavelength.

It is also noteworthy that while ordinary capacitors have a small positive temperature co-efficient (e.g. increasing in value with temperature), ceramic and specially-developed types have a larger negative temperature co-efficient. Thus by judiciously arranging a combination of the two types, a degree of frequency/temperature stability can be achieved.

A single-tuned circuit can never provide sufficient selectivity in a modern radio receiver, and for this reason a number of tuned circuits are employed, some ganged to tune in step together and others fixed-tuned.

The crystal set

The simplest receiver is the 'crystal' set, whose circuit is given in Figure 5.10. In modern guise, the old-style crystal detector is replaced by the semiconductor diode (Chapter 7); but apart from this the circuit remains just the same as at the beginnings of radio. It works like this; radio signals picked up by the aerial are applied, relative to earth, across the parallel-tuned circuit, and the variable capacitor is adjusted until the tuned circuit resonates at the frequency of the required signal.

The signal voltage of the required transmission developed across the tuned circuit will, of course, be amplitude-modulated (Chapter 2), and so will appear rather like the waveform shown in Figure 5.11(a), where the modulation is pure tone, constituting a sine-wave signal. Because the modulation envelope is symmetrical about the zero level, the wave in this form is incapable of operating a headphone set

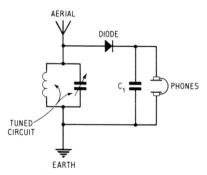

Figure 5.10. Circuit diagram of the crystal set; see text for explanation of how it works

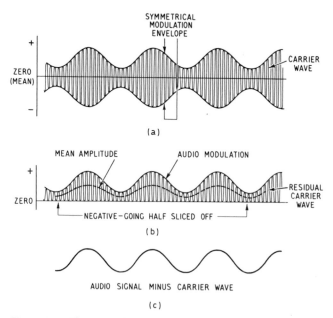

Figure 5.11. The principle of a.m. detection: (a) the a.m. waveform selected by the tuned circuit(s); (b) the rectifying action of the diode; (c) the resulting audio modulation signal, the r.f. components being removed by C_1 in Figure 5.10

113

or loudspeaker, even when greatly amplified. The wave thus needs to be rendered asymmetrical, and this process is called *demodulation* or *detection*.

A.M. detection

The crystal detector or diode achieves this merely by rectifying the a.m. signal. It is shown in Chapter 7 that a diode allows current to flow unimpeded in one direction, while blocking the flow almost completely in the opposite direction – a sort of one-way 'valve' action. After passing through the diode, therefore, the a.m. wave is effectively 'sliced' from the zero level, so that only one half remains, as shown in Figure 5.11(b). In this case it is the positive-going half of the waveform that remains, the negative-going half being removed by the lack of conduction through the diode. The direction of the arrow-head on the diode symbol implies that the conduction is in the positive direction. If the diode were reversed, the negative-going half-cycles would be passed and the positive-going half-cycles deleted. While this would change the d.c. conditions (after rectification), it would have no effect on the demodulation process.

Waveform (b) is thus asymmetrical, and because of this its mean amplitude varies in accordance with the modulation. The value of C_1 in Figure 5.10 is chosen so that it offers a low reactance to the r.f. components of the signal and a relatively high reactance to the lower-frequency audio components. The low r.f. reactance effectively 'short-circuits' the r.f. components while barely affecting the a.f. (audio modulation) components; this means that the headphone set passes a.f. current corresponding to the original modulation signal, which is heard by the listener.

All a.m. receivers incorporate a demodulator or detector that works on the principles just outlined and, indeed, most modern receivers use a semiconductor diode as the detector. The demodulation of f.m. signals is a little more involved, as shown later (page 128).

The simple crystal set demonstrates dramatically the principles of a.m. reception, and all beginners should certainly not miss the opportunity of enjoying this first adventure into radio! It will be appreciated, of course, that the sound from the headphone set will be very weak owing to the fact that all the audio power is derived from the aerial signal alone. For best results, the headphone set should be as sensitive as possible and the aerial and earth system as efficient as possible; and do not expect to get a good response from the weak signals of distant stations! The radio hobby shops sell suitable components, with coils switching over the long and medium waves, and tuning in conjunction with a 500 pF variable capacitor. Pretty well any semiconductor diode will serve for the detector, and to avoid cutting the higher audio frequencies of the modulation too much, C_1 can have a value around 1000 pF.

The circuit shown in Figure 5.10 will not be very selective. The local or regional programmes will be found to come in over a wide range of the capacitor tuning, and after dusk two or more stations will probably be received together. This is because the tuned circuit is heavily damped by the 'shunting' effect of the aerial and earth. In other words, the inductance, capacitance and resistive losses of the aerial and earth appear right across the tuned circuit, thereby significantly reducing its Q value and encouraging unwanted station breakthrough, as shown in Figure 5.12.

The selectivity can be improved either by coupling the aerial to a tapping (towards the 'earthy' end) down the main tuning coil or by introducing the aerial signal to the main tuning coil by way of an aerial coupling coil, shown respectively at (a) and (b) in Figure 5.13. Aerial damping effects can also be alleviated by connecting a capacitor in *series* with the aerial. This method also reduces the capacitive shunting of the aerial, since the net capacitance is reduced when two capacitances are connected in series (see Chapter 6).

While the damping is reduced and the selectivity enhanced by these methods, the actual signal amplitude from the output of the tuned circuit tends to diminish, which, with the simple crystal set, can significantly weaken the output from the headphone set.

The modern radio receiver is a development of the simple crystal set. That is, it has r.f. stages in front of it and a.f. stages behind it; in fact, the crystal set circuit in Figure 5.10 represents only the detector or demodulator part of the modern radio receiver. The r.f. stages are *tuned* amplifiers designed both to boost the very weak aerial signals and greatly to improve the overall selectivity relative to the mediocre selectivity provided by a single tuned circuit. As

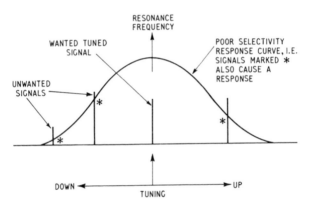

Figure 5.12. Heavy damping of the single tuned circuit of the crystal set in Figure 5.10 by the directly coupled aerial and earth will significantly impair the selectivity, so that adjacent signals, as well as the wanted signal, will be received

more tuned circuits are employed together in an integrated design, so the selectivity is improved and the skirts of the response curve steepened, requirements essential for maximum discrimination against adjacent-frequency unwanted stations.

The a.f. stages are designed to boost the weak audio signals at the output of the detector to a level sufficient to drive the loudspeaker. Indeed, the modern receiver (Chapter 10) employs transistors and solid-state devices (Chapter 7) as well as integrated circuits (Chapter 8) to achieve all these requirements.

A block diagram of a tuned radio frequency (t.r.f.) receiver is given in Figure 5.14. This employs two r.f. amplifiers, four tuned circuits, a.m. detector, a.f. amplifier and power-output stage driving the loudspeaker. The aerial signal is coupled to the first tuned circuit L_1/C_1 by the aerial coupling coil (Figure 5.13), and the signal resonated by this circuit is applied to the

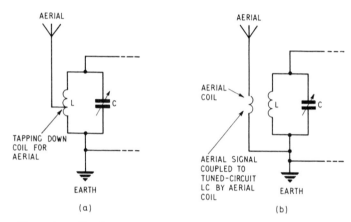

Figure 5.13. The damping on the tuned circuit from the aerial can be reduced (a) by tapping the aerial down the coil, or (b) by coupling-in the aerial signal to the main tuning coil by a separate aerial coil

first r.f. amplifier, whose output is tuned by L_2/C_2. The signal across this tuned circuit at resonance is coupled to the third tuned circuit L_3/C_3 by the transformer action between L_2 and L_3, the signal then being applied to the input of the second r.f. amplifier. The net signal gain between the aerial and the input of the second r.f. stage is shown as 50 times (about 34 dB), which takes account of the gain of the first r.f. amplifier and the coupling losses.

The second r.f. amplifier further boosts the signal, which is resonated across the fourth tuned circuit L_4/C_4, and is then coupled to the input of the a.m. detector through the detector coupling coil. The level of the audio signal at the output of the detector is given as 500 mV although, of course, it will depend not only on the gain of the second r.f. amplifier and the losses in the couplings, but also on the depth of the modulation.

The 500 mV of audio is fed to the a.f. amplifier, which gives a 10-times (20 dB) boost, and the resulting 5 V signal is fed to the power-output stage, which produces 10 W across the loudspeaker.

It will be seen that the four variable capacitors are linked by broken lines, these signifying that the four circuits are tuned together and in step; or, in other words, that the capacitors are *ganged* so that the four circuits tune exactly to the same frequency at any setting of the tuning control over the selected waveband, generally determined by coil switching. It would be possible, of course, to tune the circuits by varying the inductance of the coils, keeping the capacitor values constant (see the resonance frequency expression on page 107). This technique is, in fact, sometimes used, the inductance being varied by the movement of ferrite (iron-dust) cores in the coils, activated by the tuning control. Most receivers, though, employ ganged variable capacitors or capacitor diodes (varicaps), which are semiconductor diodes whose capacitance decreases with increase in reverse bias (see Chapter 7), the reverse bias being adjusted by a potentiometer coupled to the tuning control or push-buttons for station selection.

Tuned circuits L_2/C_2 and L_3/C_3 in Figure 5.14 constitute a bandpass coupling, which implies that the design yields a response curve embracing a specific 'band' of frequencies. It will be recalled from Chapter 2 that side frequencies or sidebands are produced by the modulation, and that these, corresponding to the highest modulation frequency transmitted, need to be passed to the detector for the best quality reception. To achieve this, while ensuring the maximum discrimination against adjacent signals and their sidebands, the top of the response curve should ideally be flat, and the side skirts swiftly falling, as shown in Figure 5.15.

This ideal is difficult to obtain in practice, but it can be approached by the use of multiple tuned circuits and

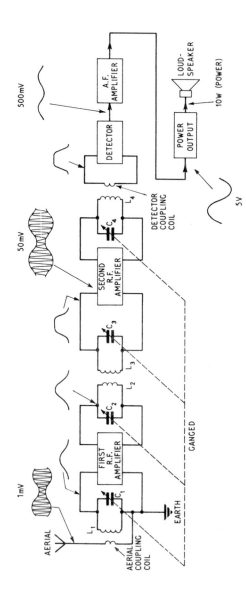

Figure 5.14. Block diagram of tuned radio frequency (t.r.f.) radio receiver (see text)

119

bandpass couplings. The curves marked along the block diagram in Figure 5.14 reveal how the response is progressively shaped, so that the response at the detector is close to the bandpass requirement. Owing to the close proximity of stations operating in the medium-frequency bands, the passband is generally deliberately restricted to avoid adjacent-station interference. This reduces the treble response at

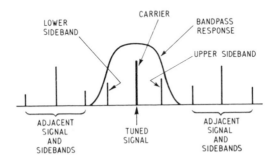

Figure 5.15. Showing how a bandpass response characteristic contains the carrier and the higher-order lower and upper sidebands while affording high discrimination against adjacent signals and their sidebands

the receiver; but, in any case, there is not much point in arranging for a much wider passband because the higher-order sidebands are suppressed at most a.m. stations (see Chapter 4) to reduce the possibility of them 'splashing' into the frequencies occupied by adjacent stations.

These comments are not applicable to the f.m. system of broadcasting because each f.m. station operates within the protection of a 200 kHz Band 2 channel. This allows the f.m. sidebands fully to develop (the requirement for low-distortion, wide-dynamic-range mono and stereo reception) without breaking into adjacent channels. This is one reason why the f.m. system of broadcasting is able to provide a far better quality of reception than the medium-frequency a.m. system.

120

Superhet receiver

There is no need for all the tuned circuits to be variable and ganged to yield the necessary degree of selectivity, as they are in the block diagram of the t.r.f. receiver (Figure 5.14). Indeed, the contemporary way of handling the selectivity requirement is by the use of a fixed-tuned *intermediate-frequency* (i.f.) channel, based on the superhet principle, another early radio development that is still very much a part of today's designs.

Superhet is short for *superheterodyne*; it means that the frequency of the tuned incoming aerial signal is converted to an intermediate frequency (generally at a lower frequency than the incoming signal) and then amplified before being applied to the detector stage. The front end of the receiver, which accomplishes this conversion, is sometimes called the *frequency changer*; this has two parts, the *mixer* and the *local oscillator*. The tuned aerial signal is applied to the mixer along with the signal generated by the local oscillator, which is a fairly pure sine wave. The two signals are thus 'mixed', and a tuned circuit or filter at the output of the mixer selects either the sum of the two or the difference between them, which corresponds to the intermediate frequency.

A block diagram of the frequency-changer or converter part of the superhet receiver is given in Figure 5.16. This shows that the incoming signal is tuned by C_1 and the local oscillator signal by C_2 (coils are present, of course, but are not shown in the simple diagram). Ganged tuning is adopted, as signified by the broken line linking C_1 and C_2, the idea being to maintain a consistent difference between f_1 and f_2 (corresponding to the i.f.) over the entire tuning range.

The 'standard' i.f. is 470 kHz for a.m. receivers and 10.7 MHz for f.m. receivers, although there may be differences, particularly in the a.m. case. In Figure 5.16 the tuned aerial signal is labelled f_1 and the tuned oscillator signal f_2, with f_3 referring to the i.f. signal. The mixing process creates two or more signals of sum and difference frequencies, such that f_3 could be $f_1 + f_2$, $f_1 - f_2$ or $f_2 - f_1$ (there are other orders, which need not bother us at this level of study).

121

The signals are produced because the mixer works rather like a modulator that is, the tuned aerial signal modulates the local oscillator signal (or vice versa), thereby yielding upper and lower sidebands at the sum and difference frequencies, the required one being selected by a tuned circuit or filter. It is important to understand that the i.f. signal carries exactly the same audio modulation as the tuned radio signal, the only difference being the difference in frequency. It will be appreciated, of course, that the i.f. remains constant, irrespective of the frequency of the tuned aerial signal.

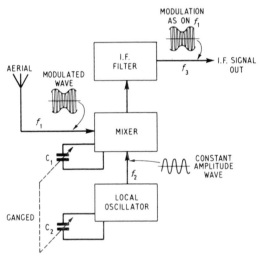

Figure 5.16. Front of the superhet, called the frequency changer or converter. The mixer and local oscillator parts work together to produce an intermediate-frequency (i.f.) signal, selected by a tuned circuit or filter at the mixer output. Tuned amplifiers boost the signal prior to its application to the detector

The frequency of the local oscillator is commonly above that of the tuned aerial signal, thereby corresponding to $f_1 + f_3$. Thus an f.m. receiver tuned, say, to 95 MHz would have its local oscillator running at 105.7 MHz (95 + 10.7). In other words, the 95 MHz tuned aerial signal mixes with the 105.7 MHz local oscillator signal, and the difference-frequency or i.f. of 10.7 MHz (i.e. $f_2 - f_1 = f_3$ or $105.7 - 95 = 10.7$) is selected. There will also be an output signal of 200.7 MHz ($f_1 + f_2$ or $95 + 105.7$), but this is strongly rejected by the i.f. tuned circuits or filters and so is not passed to the detector at any significant amplitude.

Spurious responses

The i.f. can also be produced by harmonics of the local oscillator and by harmonics of the signal frequency produced by the mixer or r.f. stage. For example, if a strong aerial signal at 100 MHz overloads the front end of an f.m. receiver, the second harmonic at 200 MHz might well be produced. Now, if the receiver is tuned to 94.65 MHz the local oscillator will be running at 105.35 MHz. If the local oscillator also has a second-harmonic output, this will be at 210.7 MHz which, when mixed with the 200 MHz second harmonic of the input signal, will produce the 10.7 MHz i.f. This is called the *half i.f. response* or sometimes *repeat spot response*. A very strong signal at the i.f. may also break through the mixer and give a continuous output, irrespective of the tuning control setting. This is called the i.f. response.

Image response

This is another important spurious response, which falls at two times the i.f. above the receiver-tuned frequency when the local oscillator frequency is above that of the incoming signal, and at two times the i.f. below when the frequency of the local oscillator is below the incoming frequency. Suppose an f.m. receiver is tuned to 95 MHz, the oscillator (when above the signal frequency) will then be running at 105.7 MHz. The main response occurs, as we have seen, from $105.7 - 95 = 10.7$ MHz. However, another response producing the 10.7 MHz i.f. will occur from an input signal at

116.4 MHz, because 116.4 − 105.7 = 10.7 MHz. This is the *image* or *second channel* response.

All these spurious responses are reduced by the selectivity of the signal-frequency tuning in front of the mixer. In other words, the better the selectivity at the front of the receiver, the greater the discrimination against off-tune input signals corresponding to the spurious responses. There is always at least one variable-tuned circuit between the aerial and mixer; but for better spurious response rejection two, three or sometimes more variable-tuned circuits are used in top-flight receivers.

R.F. amplifiers may also be used to boost the weak aerial signals before being applied to the mixer; they also facilitate the introduction of extra tuned circuits. Tuning over the bands is either by ganged variable capacitors (with the necessary number of sections for the r.f. stage(s), mixer and local oscillator tuning) or by varicap diodes, one for each tuned circuit and all biased together by a potentiometer, as already noted.

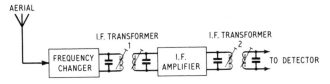

Figure 5.17. In the simplest case, bandpass transformer coupling is used between the frequency changer and i.f. amplifier and from the i.f. amplifier to the detector

Main selectivity and amplification occur in the i.f. channel, which, in its simplest form, consists merely of a single amplifier stage with tuned bandpass couplings from the mixer and to the detector, as shown in Figure 5.17. Because the i.f. remains constant, the i.f. tuning is fixed, though preset capacitors or inductors allow for initial alignment. Recent receivers employ integrated circuit (i.c.) amplifiers and piezoelectric filters (see Chapter 10), the latter working in conjunction with LC couplings (see also Chapter 6).

When a number of tuned circuits are employed, the overall response curve depends upon their alignment and coupling. Curve (a) in Figure 5.18 shows how the response tends to peak when all the circuits are adjusted exactly to the same frequency; curve (b) illustrates the practical response of a

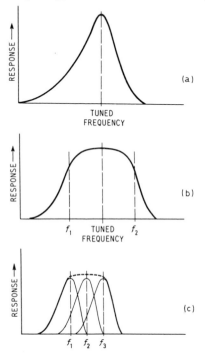

Figure 5.18. Response curves obtained from several tuned circuits: (a) all circuits tuned to the same frequency; (b) bandpass coupling; (c) stagger tuning (see text)

bandpass coupling, which responds fairly evenly to all frequencies between f_1 and f_2; while curve (c) shows how a bandpass characteristic can be obtained by tuning several circuits slightly to different frequencies. This is called *stagger tuning*.

A tuned circuit has its maximum response at the resonance frequency (f_0), and this applies particularly to a single tuned circuit since the response of specially staggered and tailored tuned and coupled circuits may be fairly 'flat' over the top of the response curve. The width of a response curve, otherwise known as the *bandwidth* of the tuned circuit, is defined as the frequency distance between the side-skirt levels where the response is 0.707 ($1/\sqrt{2}$) of the maximum response.

There is a relationship between the Q-factor of a tuned circuit and its bandwidth, such that $Q = f_0/f_h - f_1$, where f_h and f_1 are the highest and lowest frequencies respectively of the response curve at the level already noted, or $f_0/f_2 \Delta f$. This indicates that the bandwidth is inversely proportional to the Q-factor – or that the higher the Q-factor the less the bandwidth.

A block diagram of an f.m./a.m. receiver is given in Figure 5.19. The power-supply section (not shown) is common to both f.m. and a.m., as also are the output stages. On a.m., of course, both output stages and loudspeakers carry the mono signal, while on f.m. and stereo the left and right signals are handled by separate output stages and loudspeakers, as controlled by the f.m./a.m. switching.

Apart from the common sections, the f.m. and a.m. circuits are separate. The f.m. department (at the top) has an r.f. amplifier with aerial input tuning, bandpass coupling to the mixer, and local oscillator tuning, involving three variable-tuned circuits to the mixer and one for the oscillator. The i.f. output of the mixer is matched by the two capacitors to the first 10.7 MHz i.f. filter, after which the signal is boosted by the first i.c. Further selectivity is provided by the second 10.7 MHz i.f. filter, after which the signal is further boosted, limited (to delete amplitude variations) and then detected. The resulting output, which is a multiplex signal in the case of stereo, is fed to the stereo decoder i.c., yielding left and right audio signals. These signals are amplified separately and then fed to the left and right loudspeakers, after being selected by the f.m./a.m. switching and power-boosted by the left and right output stages.

126

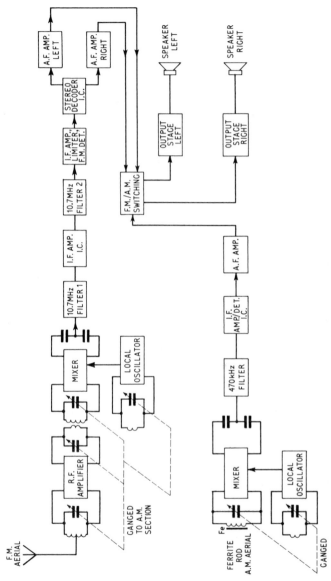

Figure 5.19. Block diagram of f.m./a.m. receiver (see text)

127

The a.m. department has a ferrite-rod aerial (see Chapter 3) working straight into the mixer which, along with the local oscillator, is tuned by the ganged capacitor. The i.f. output from the mixer is matched to the 470 kHz filter, again by two capacitors, and then amplified and detected by an i.c. The a.f. output from the i.c. is further amplified, and then fed to the two power-output stages and loudspeakers by the f.m./a.m. switching.

Detail may differ between receivers. For example, the mixer and oscillator functions particularly on a.m., may be handled by a single transistor stage, there may be more or fewer i.c.s involved, depending on the receiver's vintage, and LC bandpass couplings may be used exclusively or in partnership with piezoelectric filters in the i.f. channels.

Communications and amateur receivers sometimes employ several mixers and i.f. channels to improve spurious response rejection and selectivity.

There are several parts of the circuit that we have not yet covered in detail, such as the piezoelectric filters, the i.c.s, including the stereo decoder, and f.m. detection. The i.c.s are dealt with in Chapter 8 and the piezoelectric filter in Chapter 10. To conclude this chapter outlining principles, therefore, let us look briefly at f.m. detection and stereo decoding.

F.M. detection

F.M. detection is more involved than a.m. detection, which, as we have seen, is usually based on a single diode. Excluding for the moment the type of f.m. detection provided by certain i.c.s, which is looked at in Chapter 8, many f.m. receivers and tuners incorporate circuits in which two diodes are used in one of the configurations given at (a) and (b) in Figure 5.20. That at (a) is known as a *Foster-Seeley f.m. detector* or discriminator, while that at (b) is the *ratio detector*.

Looking first at (a), T_1 couples the f.m. signal (at i.f.) from the transistor collector to diodes D_1 and D_2, which involves another factor of tuned and coupled circuits that we have not

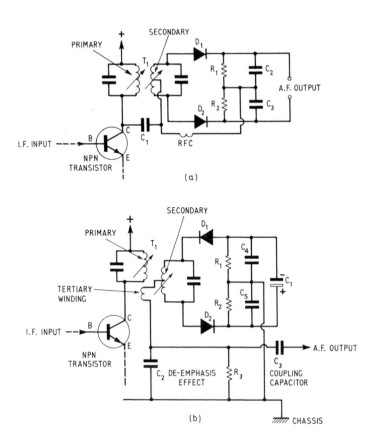

Figure 5.20. F.M. detector circuits: (a) Foster-Seeley where the two diodes are arranged back-to-back and phase-reference capacitor C_1 is used; and (b) ratio detector where the two diodes are arranged in series and tertiary-phase reference winding is used. An unbalanced version of this circuit will also be found in some f.m. receivers (see text)

yet looked at. When the primary and secondary are tuned exactly to the frequency of the carrier, there is a predictable 90-degree phase displacement between the signals across the two windings (see Figure 5.5). A phase reference is coupled to the centre-tap of the secondary from the collector of the

129

transistor through C_1, so the overall effect is that D_1 and D_2 conduct equally on steady carrier signal. Thus the d.c. voltage across R_1 is equal, but of opposite polarity, to that developed across R_2. Since the sum of two opposing but equal voltages is zero, there is zero output across the a.f. terminals.

Now, when the carrier is frequency-modulated, the balanced state is destroyed because the frequency of the signal deviates about the tuned frequency of T_1. Depending upon the deviation and hence the modulation, one diode tends to conduct more than the other, with the result that the voltages across R_1 and R_2 no longer resolve to zero. An alternating signal voltage corresponding to the original modulation signal is thus developed across the a.f. output terminals. The r.f. signal is 'blocked' from the output by the high reactance of the r.f. choke and further filtered by the low reactance of C_2 and C_3, relative to the higher reactance presented to the audio component. The greater the *rate* of deviation, the higher the audio frequency; and the greater the extent of the deviation, the greater the audio output voltage (a.f. signal).

The two diodes of the ratio detector at (b) are effectively in series (not opposing as are those in the other diagram), which means that the i.f. signal across the secondary of T_1 is rectified and a steady carrier d.c. is developed across R_1 and R_2 in series, charging the electrolytic capacitor C_1. Instead of C_1 at (a), the ratio detector uses a *tertiary* (meaning third) winding between the primary of T_1 and the centre-tap of the secondary. Since the coupling between the primary and the tertiary winding is tight and the tertiary winding is untuned, the voltage across the teritary winding holds in phase with that across the primary, but is 90 degrees out of phase with that across the secondary when T_1 is tuned to the nominal i.f. The centre of the secondary is given a phase reference from the tertiary, in rather the same way as the centre of T_1's secondary in circuit (a) is given a phase reference from C_1.

Now, when the signal is frequency-modulated, the phase of the signal across the secondary deviates relative to the centre-tap, with the result that the signal across the tertiary winding *adds* to the signal across one half of the secondary and *subtracts* from the signal across the other half. The deviation rate, of course, is at audio frequency and, since the diodes are series-connected through the secondary and loads R_1/R_2, an unbalance current at a.f. flows out of the circuit through the tertiary winding and C_2. In other words, the modulation signal develops across the reactance of C_2.

Amplitude limiting (time-constants)

As we have seen, the d.c. across R_1 and R_2 in series charges C_1, whose symbol indicates that it is an electrolytic capacitor (see Chapter 6). Its value is relatively high, therefore, and in conjunction with the load resistors R_1/R_2 it endows the circuit with an electronic 'flywheel' effect. The time taken for C_1 to charge and discharge (as, for example, resulting from the input i.f. signal being switched on and then off) depends on both the value of the capacitor and the total value of the resistance across it. This is expressed as a time-constant which, in seconds, is equal to CR, where C is in farads and R in ohms. Thus if C_1 is, say $4\,\mu\text{F}$ and $R_1 + R_2 = 27\,000$ ohms, the time-constant would be $4 \times 10^{-6} \times 27 \times 10^3 = 0.1\,\text{s}$, which is the time taken for 63.2 per cent charge or discharge. (It takes five times the time-constant for 99.5 per cent charge or discharge.)

   Relative to rapid variations in amplitude of the input i.f. signal (caused, for example, by electrical interference), this sort of time-constant is long, which means that the circuit neatly and automatically irons out amplitude variations on the f.m. signal, thereby providing amplitude limiting. Amplitude limiting is also included in the i.f. channel of better-class f.m. receivers, as shown in Figure 5.19.

De-emphasis

Radio circuits bristle with time-constant networks, another being formed by C_2 and R_3 in Figure 5.20(b). This, in fact, is the de-emphasis network, which is a feature of f.m. receivers (see page 87 and Figure 4.5). For the British and European

50 μs time-constant, C_2 could be 5 nF (i.e. 5×10^{-9} F) and R_3 10 kilohms. However, in practice associated components tend to modify the nature of the network and thus have to be taken into account when computing the component values.

Transformer T_1 at (a) and (b) in Figure 5.20 uses fixed capacitors across primary and secondary, the tuning or alignment being performed by adjusting the inductance by iron-dust cores. Capacitors C_4 and C_5 in (b) serve the same purpose as capacitors C_2 and C_3 in (a). C_3 in (b) couples the audio signal to subsequent stages while blocking the d.c. component; such coupling would also be adopted with circuit (a). The ratio detector at (b) is balanced about the chassis by virtue of the split load R_1/R_2 whose junction is connected to chassis. The circuit is sometimes unbalanced, with a single resistor in shunt with C_1 and possibly without C_4 and C_5; the positive side of C_1 is then usually connected direct to chassis.

'S' characteristic

The response curve of an f.m. detector is given in Figure 5.21. Owing to its shape, this is often referred to as the 'S' characteristic. For maximum linearity, and hence least distortion, the deviation of the signal occurs over the middle portion of the characteristic. The overall bandwidth of the detector in a high grade receiver is wider than that of the i.f. channel, sometimes approaching 1 MHz.

Stereo decoding

Decoding is the opposite to encoding – dealt with in Chapter 4 – and an f.m. receiver with a decoder will 'unscramble' the encoded signal to produce separate left and right stereo signals. Without a decoder, the receiver will treat the encoded signal as a mono signal and thus produce a correctly balanced single-channel output. The decoder is connected to the output of the f.m. detector, and to prevent the high-frequency components of the multiplex (stereo) signal from being attenuated by the de-emphasis, this is generally moved to the output of the decoder as shown in Figure 5.22.

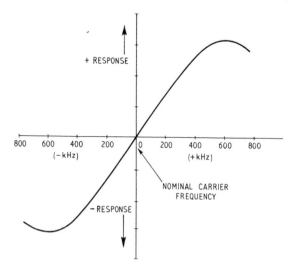

Figure 5.21. The 'S' characteristic of an f.m. detector. Signal deviation is confined to the middle (linear) part of the curve for least distortion. The d.c. output is sometimes used for automatic frequency control

A block diagram of one kind of decoder is given in Figure 5.23. The stereo multiplex signal from the detector (see Figure 4.10) is filtered into its three components, which are the mono A + B signal, the stereo A − B sidebands and the 19 kHz pilot tone. The frequency of the pilot tone is doubled to reclaim the 38 kHz subcarrier – which, it will be recalled, was deliberately suppressed at the transmitter, and without which A − B detection would not be possible. From the A − B stereo *sidebands* and the reclaimed 38 kHz subcarrier, the synchronous detector yields A − B *audio* information when the phase of the reclaimed subcarrier correlates with that of the transmitter's subcarrier. When the decoder circuits are

133

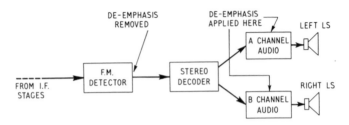

Figure 5.22. The stereo decoder is connected to the output of the f.m. detector after removal of the de-emphasis

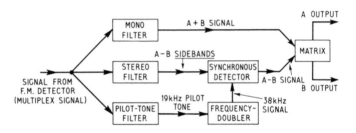

Figure 5.23. Block diagram one kind of stereo decoder. There are other kinds, including the i.c. decoder which is extensively used

correctly adjusted the phasing must be correct because (Chapter 4) the transmitter's subcarrier was obtained by doubling the frequency of the pilot tone in the first place. Under this condition the A − B detector works synchronously (hence its name), and the A − B and A + B audio signals are fed to the matrix.

As explained in Chapter 4, the matrix applies both addition and subtraction to the two lots of signals, thereby producing the A (left) signal in one channel and the B (right) signal in the other channel.

There are various other types of stereo decoders, the most recent ones being based on integrated circuits (see Chapter 8).

6

Radio components

The component parts of radio equipment can be classified as *passive* or *active*. Passive components are such things as resistors, capacitors, inductors, and the interconnecting conductors of the circuit or network itself. The main active components are transistors, valves and batteries. While a receiver can be made entirely from passive components (the 'crystal' receiver for example), all contemporary radio equipment uses both passive and active components. This chapter deals essentially with passive components, subsequent chapters looking at transistors, integrated circuits and valves.

Resistance

When electrons are caused to flow in a circuit as the result of an e.m.f., the current flow is inhibited by the resistance of the circuit; that is, the flow of electrons is impeded by collision with the atoms comprising the circuit. The result is temperature rise and hence power loss. The effect is called resistance which, as we have already noted, is measured in ohms, often signified by the Greek letter omega (Ω).

The resistivity, of a material is a function of the number of mobile electrons available for current carrying, which means that a material of a given resistivity will reduce in resistance as its cross-sectional area is increased. A good analogy is a water pipe – the larger the diameter or cross-sectional area of the pipe, the greater the volume of water that can flow.

Where a high current is required to be carried with minimal heating and hence power loss, conductors of large cross-sectional area need to be employed. The starter motor of a motor car, for example, passes a large current at relatively low voltage, so to get the necessary power to the motor a short cable of large diameter is employed. In other words, the resistance of the cable is very small.

The resistance of a conductor is proportional to its length and inversely proportional to its cross-sectional area. Actual resistance also depends upon the material and its temperature. Some conducting elements have a positive temperature coefficient and others a negative one – the former increasing in resistance with temperature and the latter decreasing in resistance with temperature (see later).

Resistors

In radio circuits it is often necessary to limit and control the current flow, which calls for the deliberate insertion of

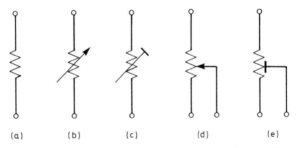

(a)   (b)   (c)   (d)   (e)

Figure 6.1. Resistor symbols: (a) fixed resistor, (b) variable resistor, (c) preset variable resistor, (d) potentiometer and (e) preset potentiometer. When two or more variable resistors are ganged, a broken line couples the sliders

resistance into the circuits. A component known as a *resistor* (R) performs this function, and its symbol is shown in Figure 6.1(a).

Over the years many kinds of resistors have been evolved to satisfy the wide and varied requirements of the designer.

136

One of the simplest resistors is the wire-wound variety, which employs resistance wire (wire of a greater resistivity than, for example, copper) wound on a ceramic former. Wire-wound resistors are used where the power to be lost is large. They are thus designed to withstand a significant rise in temperature. Maximum power dissipation of a resistor is the amount of power in watts (W) that it can continuously translate to heat without burning out or changing in value. A resistor that is likely to operate warm or hot must be located in the equipment with due regard to ventilation, and where the power to be lost is very high the heat has to be dissipated by heat sinks. If overheated, a resistor can change significantly in value, and on cooling it may not recover its original value. The maximum dissipation of a resistor is commonly given as a temperature parameter, above which the power must be reduced or the resistor replaced with one of higher power rating, a common value being 70°C.

The two main parameters of a resistor, therefore, are resistance value in ohms and power rating in watts. If a low-wattage resistor is used in a circuit that requires a large power dissipation the resistor will get very hot, change value and burn out.

In many parts of a radio circuit the power loss is very small, which means that physically small, low-wattage resistors can be employed without danger of overheating. A common species for this purpose is the carbon-composition resistor. This consists of a pressed mixture of carbon, ceramic dust and resin, developed at high temperature into the form of a rod, with leadout connecting electrodes at the ends.

Resistors are sorted into tolerance ranges and thus classified, thereby giving resistance tolerance ranges of 10 – 20 per cent and 5 – 10 per cent. Critical circuits may require even closer-tolerance components, and these are more expensive than those suitable for the less critical circuits. Carbon-composition resistors are generally available over a value range from 2.2 ohms to 22 megohms and a power range from as small as 0.125 W to 3 or 5 W.

Various other forms of 'carbon' resistors are available, including high-stability carbon film, moulded carbon, etc.

Film resistors are comparatively new, the conducting film being of carbon, tin oxide or other metal, depending on the requirements. The film is very thin and is formed on the surface of a rod of porcelain or glass, and the required value is accurately adjusted by the cutting of a spiral track in the film. Film resistors can be obtained with fine tolerances, right down to 0.1 per cent for very critical applications. Variations include thick film, metal film, metal oxide, etc. This latest type of resistor is more tolerant of resistance change with change in temperature than the earlier carbon-composition type of resistor.

There is also a wide variety of wire-wound resistors based on some kind of resistance wire, such as nickel and chromium alloys. Since the winding of resistance wire produces inductance, non-inductive wire-wound resistors are made by winding in opposite directions: that is, by winding in the form of a double spiral, so that the current flows first in one direction and then back in the opposite direction, a technique that neutralises the inductance.

Wire-wound resistors can operate at much higher temperatures than the carbon and film species, some up to 300°C surface temperature. There are various configurations, including self-supporting vitreous components, and types that need special supports and, perhaps, heat sinks to dissipate the heat. Wire-wound resistors are usually of a lower resistance value than the other types mentioned.

Temperature coefficient

Another resistor parameter is *temperature coefficient*, which signifies how the resistance changes with temperature. When it rises with temperature, which is a characteristic of many metals, the term *positive* temperature coefficient (p.t.c.) is used; conversely, a *negative* temperature coefficient (n.t.c.) is indicated when the resistance falls as the temperature rises. Some resistors are made specifically to exploit these effects; but for many normal applications a significant change in resistance with temperature is not desirable.

The parameter is expressed as so many parts per million (ppm) change for each degree Celsius change in temperature. A resistor of, say 100 ppm/°C temperature coefficient would thus change by 1000 ppm (or by 0.1 per cent) for a 10°C rise in temperature. Thus, a resistor of 1 MΩ nominal value would change by 1 kΩ over the 10°C temperature rise, upwards with a p.t.c. and downwards with an n.t.c.

Resistors also need to be selected to suit the maximum potential difference likely to develop across them, and to suit the noise requirements of the circuit; for example, high-gain hi-fi amplifiers need to be designed for low-background-noise operation, so the resistors used in the critical parts of these circuits need to be low-noise type. As we have already noted, the movement of electrons constitutes a flow of electricity; the random movement (or 'vibration') of electrons produces random noise, which manifests itself as 'hiss' from the loudspeakers connected to high-gain amplifiers. The noise depends on the value of the resistors, on their temperature and on the bandwidth of the circuits. Film resistors usually have a lower noise value than carbon composition resistors.

Resistor colour code

Some examples of fixed resistors are shown in Figure 6.2, and their values are identified by the first three bands of a special colour code, as shown in Figure 6.3. There is also a fourth band of red, gold or silver indicating the tolerance; the lack of a band here indicates a tolerance of 20 per cent. A 1 MΩ resistor of, say, 10 per cent tolerance means that it could lie anywhere within the range 1 MΩ ± 100 000 ohms (100 kΩ), i.e. from 999 kΩ to 1.1 MΩ.

A resistor with a value colour code of brown, black and red indicates that the first digit is 1, the second digit 0, followed by 2 zeros, making a total value of (1) (0) (00), or 1 kΩ (1000 ohms). High-stability resistors often have a salmon-pink body.

A system of preferred values for resistors has been evolved by the radio industry, the ranges being dictated by the

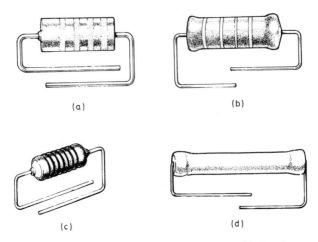

Figure 6.2. Examples of fixed resistors: (a) moulded carbon, (b) high-stability carbon film, (c) ceramic-former wire-wound, and (d) cement-coated self-supporting wire-wound

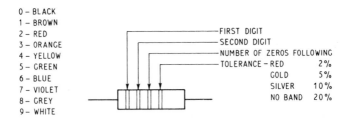

Figure 6.3. Resistor colour code (see text)

tolerances, as shown in Table 6.1. The values given in the table correspond to all the decades, so that 2.2, for example, could be 2.2 ohms, 22 ohms, 220 ohms, 2.2 kΩ, 22 kΩ, 220 kΩ, 2.2 MΩ, and perhaps 22.2 MΩ, but the values normally available stop in the megohm decade. It is also possible to obtain specific-value resistors, but these are more costly than those of preferred values.

Table 6.1. Preferred values of resistors

±5%	Tolerance ±10%	±20%
1.0	1.0	1.0
1.1		
1.2	1.2	
1.5	1.5	1.5
1.6		
1.8	1.8	
2.0		
2.2	2.2	2.2
2.4		
2.7	2.7	
3.0		
3.3	3.3	3.3
3.6		
3.9	3.9	
4.3		
4.7	4.7	4.7
5.1		
5.6	5.6	
6.2		
6.8	6.8	6.8
7.5		
8.2		
9.1		

Resistors in series and parallel

When a number of resistors are connected in series (e.g. in line with one another), the total resistance (R_t) is the arithmetical sum of their individual values such as $R_t = R1 + R2 + R3$ ... etc.

When a number of resistors are connected in parallel (in shunt with one another), the total resistance works out to

141

$1/R_t = 1/R1 + 1/R2 + 1/R3$ ... etc. In other words, the reciprocal of R_t is equal to the sum of the reciprocals of each resistor in parallel. When there are just two resistors connected in parallel, R_t can be found from $(R1 \times R2)/(R1 + R2)$.

Resistors are often connected in series and/or parallel to obtain a specific value that cannot be readily obtained from a single resistor. The power rating of the combination is also increased because in the series mode the voltage across each is reduced and in the parallel mode the current flowing through each is reduced, bearing in mind that the power dissipated in watts (W) is equal to E^2/R and I^2R.

Thermistors and non-linear resistors

A *thermistor* is a resistor that is designed specifically to change in value with change in temperature. These are sometimes used for valve heater-current control to prevent current surges when the receiver is first switched on. Such a

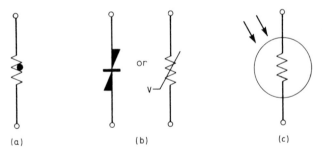

Figure 6.4. Special resistor symbols: (a) n.t.c. thermistor (p.t.c. indicated when small circle used in place of black dot), (b) voltage-dependent resistor, and (c) light-dependent resistor

component has an n.t.c and is relatively high in value when cold, thereby limiting the surge current. As it warms up so its value falls, so that the current is gradually increased following switch-on, rather than generating a surge, which can be harmful to the heaters of valves in series-connected circuits. The symbol of this kind of resistor is given in Figure 6.4(a). When the black dot is replaced by a small open circle, a p.t.c. is indicated.

Thermistors and resistors with carefully controlled n.t.c. and p.t.c. properties are also used in other circuits, including oscillator circuits to combat frequency change with change in temperature and hence value of components, and in transistor and solid-state circuits.

A pure resistor has a linear voltage/current characteristic that follows Ohm's Law. Some resistors, however, are designed deliberately to have a non-linear characteristic. A so-called *voltage-dependent resistor* (v.d.r.) is a good example; this is often used for surge suppression and for eliminating dangerous voltage peaks. Up to a certain voltage such a resistor has a high value; when this voltage is exceeded, however, the value tends sharply to fall, thereby inhibiting voltage peaks across the circuit that it shunts, without affecting the normal-voltage operation of the circuit. The symbols for this type of resistor are shown in Figure 6.4(b).

Another resistor that has optical characteristics is the *light-dependent resistor* (l.d.r.), whose symbols are given in Figure 6.4(c). In a dark place such a resistor will have a high value, and a reducing value as more light is allowed to fall upon it.

Variable resistors and potentiometers

Variable resistors and potentiometers are used for the main and preset controls of radio circuits, a typical main control being that for volume or 'gain' in audio amplifiers and in the audio sections of radio receivers. The symbols of these components are given in Figure 6.1, and signify that there is a fixed resistive element along which operates a wiper or slider allowing the resistance to be adjusted by a control spindle and knob (main control) or screwdriver slot. An arrow-head indicates a main control, while a 'T' shape means that the control is of the preset type, requiring a screwdriver or some other tool for adjustment.

Variable resistors (Figure 6.1 *b*, *c*) have two connections, from the slider and from one end only of the resistive element. The main control at (d) and the preset at (e) have connections at both ends of the resistive element as well as at the slider. These are *potentiometers* as distinct from variable resistors. It is usual, however, for all such controls to be equipped with connections at both ends of the resistive element, so that if it is required to use the control purely as a variable resistor then only one of the resistive element connections is used. The other is either left unconnected or is joined to the slider connection.

Whether the control operates as a variable resistor or potentiometer is thus determined by its mode of connection to the circuit. With a potentiometer the signal source (for example) is applied right across the resistive element and the output is obtained from the slider relative to the 'earthy' side of the resistive element, as shown in Figure 6.5(a). With the slider adjusted to the 'earthy' side of the resistive element, therefore, the output is zero; the output gradually increases

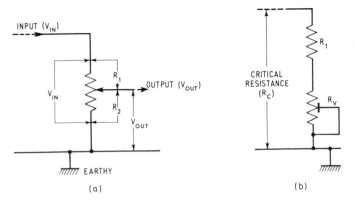

Figure 6.5. (a) Potentiometer circuit where $V_{out} = V_{in} \times R_2/(R_1 + R_2)$. A fixed potential divider uses fixed resistors for R_1 and R_2, of a ratio to give the required output from a given input voltage. (b) Variable resistor circuit. Here the critical resistance requirement is met by R_1 in series with R_v, R_v thus being adjusted to optimise the condition, where $R_c = R_1 + R_v$

as the slider is adjusted upwards as it 'samples' more and more signal voltage across the resistive element, until the maximum output occurs when the slider is in contact with the signal-input side of the resistive element. This is a typical volume or gain control action.

Figure 6.5(b) shows the connection of a preset potentiometer as a variable resistor. Here R_1 may be a very critical value that cannot be obtained within the tolerance range. Thus by including the variable resistor R_v in series the circuit can be adjusted very accurately to suit the requirements.

Preset controls are sometimes called *trimmers*, a term that is more often adopted when the component consists of a carbon-composition bar or wire-wound resistive-element bar carrying a third contact which is adjustable by hand (sometimes first by releasing a locking screw).

Figure 6.6. Example of preset controls: the type the pen is pointing to is sometimes called a skeleton preset, while the other at the left-hand side is enclosed and sometimes used as an 'edge' control

Slider main-control potentiometers are also used in some hi-fi equipment, and in studio equipment such as control desks and microphone mixers. Two trimmers are shown in

Figure 6.6 (the pen is pointing to one, and the other is adjacent to the electrolytic capacitor at the left-hand side of the photo).

Variable resistors and potentiometers are made in both carbon-composition and wire-wound varieties, the latter having the highest wattage ratings, and selection must be made to suit the power requirements of the circuit. Ordinary volume-control potentiometers rarely handle much power, so the carbon-composition type is commonly employed for this purpose. Like fixed resistors, therefore, the variable resistor and potentiometer have parameters of resistance value (which is the maximum track value) and power rating. There is also another parameter that is particularly applicable to the volume-control potentiometer, namely the *law of resistance change* as the control is adjusted.

Law of resistance change

The law is *linear* when equal change in resistance value occurs with equal increments of adjustment. For the volume control such a law is undesirable owing to the logarithmic response of the human ear. Thus for volume-control application a *logarithmic* law is commonly used. For more specialised applications controls are made with other laws, such as antilog, semilog, B-law, sine, cosine, etc. When replacing a control, therefore, it is important to choose one of the correct law.

The tolerance of carbon composition potentiometers is commonly 20 per cent, and small presets can handle up to about 50 V, while the larger components are suitable for 500 V or so. The wire-wound variety rarely go to very high values owing to the very fine resistance wire that would be required, the top value being in the region of 150 kΩ. Carbon type, however, are made up to 5 MΩ and down to about 100 ohms.

Ganged potentiometers are found in the two stereo channels of hi-fi amplifiers for control of volume, tone, and sometimes loudness and balance. Figure 6.7 shows a row of such controls on the front panel of a hi-fi amplifier. A single

146

Figure 6.7. Example of ganged potentiometers in a row on the front panel of a hi-fi amplifier. A wafer-based rotary selection switch can be seen at the extreme left-hand side

control knob operates both controls of the gang simultaneously, thus avoiding the use of separate controls for the left and right channels. High-quality controls of this kind need to be very carefully matched to ensure even change in volume, tone, etc. of the two channels. While good matching is not difficult at the higher settings of the controls, imbalance tends to increase as the controls are turned down for low-level listening.

Switches

Radio equipment employs a multitude of switching arrangements, from the simple on/off switch to the very complex source-selection or functions switch. Switches can be lever or rotary operated. A variation of the lever switch is the press-button press-key operated switch.

The contacts must be capable of handling the power that is to be switched, so fairly substantial contacts are used on the mains on/off switch, where the power can be several amperes at 240 V. The contacts of the switches in signal circuits are less critical in this respect, but the action must be positive, with low contact resistance and minimum self- and inter-capacitance to avoid attenuation of the high frequencies or crosstalk between the two channels of a stereo amplifier, for example.

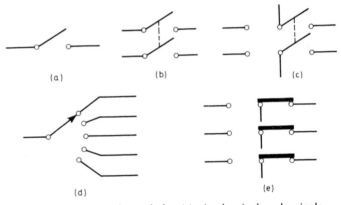

Figure 6.8. Some switch symbols: (a) simple single-pole single-throw on/off switch, (b) double-pole single-throw, (c) double-pole double-throw, (d) selector switch (often based on wafers and ganged), and (e) another example of multiple changeover switch. Switches (a) and (b) are sometimes fitted to the rear of volume controls for power on/off, the latter for mains on/off to isolate both live and neutral circuits

Complex switching is often developed by the ganging of rotary wafer switches (for example, the switch in Figure 6.7); depending on the complexity of the wafers, a large number of switching actions can be achieved by way of a single control knob. Some examples of switch symbols are given in Figure 6.8.

Capacitors

A capacitor (C) is a component with the ability to store electricity; its property is *capacitance*, expressed in sub-multiples of the *farad* (F). The farad is a very large unit; it

148

denotes the value of capacitance that will acquire a charge of one coulomb from a potential of one volt. In radio circuits we use capacitors of μF (μ standing for micro, i.e. 10^{-6}), nF (n standing for nano, i.e. 10^{-9}) and pF (p standing for pico, i.e. 10^{-12}) values.

The amount of charge capable of being held is a measure of the capacitance. Even a wire can have capacitance relative, say to earth, which is called *self-capacitance*; it is usually very small, however.

The simplest capacitor, consisting of two conducting mediums or plates in proximity, with air between them, is shown in Figure 6.9 together with its circuit symbol. When

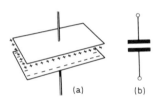

Figure 6.9. (a) Elementary capacitor formed by two plates in proximity, with air between them; the air is the dielectric and the plates acquire positive and negative charges when connected across a source of direct voltage. (b) Circuit symbol

connected across a supply of electricity (i.e. a battery) one plate acquires a surplus of electrons, while there is a shortage of electrons on the other plate owing to their being repelled by the electrons on the other plate. Thus the plates charge negatively and positively, and this charge remains when the supply is removed. In other words, the potential across the two plates (ignoring radiation and other losses) remains the same as the potential of the supply. By connecting a conductor across the two plates of a charged capacitor there will be a flow of electrons and hence an electric current, which will diminish until the electrons are balanced between the two plates.

As already noted, the term *coulomb* denotes the unit of charge (the charge is one coulomb when one ampere of current flows for one second). The amount of charge that is lost in a given time when a charged capacitor is connected in parallel with a conductor is the product of the discharge current and the time, while the total amount of current

149

required fully to charge a capacitor from its totally discharged state is $Q = CV$, where Q is the quantity of charge in coulombs, C the capacitance in farads, and V the voltage.

A capacitor charges exponentially and the *time-constant* of a CR circuit is the time that it takes a capacitor to charge to 63 per cent of the supply voltage. Time constant is the product of C and R in seconds, where C is in farads and R in ohms. It is noteworthy that the voltage across a capacitor is zero when the current is maximum, and *vice versa*. Current reaches zero after close to $5 \times CR$ seconds, the capacitor then being charged virtually as much as it ever will be!

When the voltage is direct the charge remains, but when it is alternating there are continuous charge/discharge cycles, and the amount of a.c. that flows depends on the value of the capacitor, the value of the voltage and the frequency of the a.c. In other words, a capacitor has an a.c. resistance, called capacitive reactance (X_c), which follows the normal laws of Dr Ohm. This property of the capacitor was investigated near the beginning of Chapter 5.

When a voltage is first applied to a discharge capacitor the current is maximum; current falls as the charge is acquired, being zero in the fully charged condition. Conversely, the voltage across a capacitor is minimum when it is fully discharged and the current is maximum; voltage rises as the capacitor charges and is maximum in the fully charged state, when the current is zero. These effects cause the current through a capacitor when the supply is alternating to reach its peak a quarter of a cycle (90 degrees) earlier than the peak of the voltage. In other words, the voltage across a capacitor lags the current by 90 degrees at all times. Because of this, a perfect capacitor has no power loss whatever, which is demonstrated by the fact that when the voltage is at maximum the current is zero, and vice versa.

Thus, if (by using the X_c formula at the beginning of Chapter 5) we found that the reactance of a capacitor was, say, about 30 ohms at 50 Hz (the mains supply frequency), indicating a capacitor of about 100 μF, and we connected a suitable loss-free capacitor across, say, a 50 V 50 Hz supply, there would be zero power loss in the capacitor. In a pure resistor, where the current and voltage are in phase (rising and falling together), the power loss would, from Ohm's Law, be $W = V^2/R$, which at 50 V and 30 ohms works out to $50^2/30$, i.e. about 83 W.

Also from Ohm's Law, the current through both the resistor and capacitor would be $I = V/R$ ($I = V/X_c$ in the case of the capacitor), i.e. 50/30, which works out to about 1.6 A. Because of the 90-degree voltage/current phase displacement of X_c, the power would be zero.

In practice there are bound to be losses, albeit small ones, so some power would be dissipated in these. Power loss is given by the cosine of the angle (ϕ) of voltage/current phase displacement, in terms of $W = \cos \phi\, VI$. At 90 degrees the cosine is zero, so the power is also zero. The angle falls from 90 degrees as resistive losses increase, and the angle can be computed from $\tan^{-1} X_c/R$. Thus, if the capacitor just referred to had a resistive loss of, say, 10 ohms (series), we get the little sum of $\tan^{-1} 30/10$, which works out close to 72 degrees. Putting this in the $\cos \phi\, VI$ expression we obtain $0.3\, VI$, where 0.3 is the approximate cosine of 72 degrees. This implies that the power loss is about 30 per cent of that which would be lost across a pure resistor of the same value as X_c.

Dielectric

The air across the plates in the simple capacitor in Figure 6.9 is called the *dielectric*. This, along with the surface area of the plates, determines the capacitance. The spacing between the plates also has a bearing on the capacitance value. When a dielectric other than air is used, the capacitance increases, and the amount of the increase relative to the value for air is a measure of the dielectric's *permeability*. Mica, for example, has a fairly high permeability and paraffin wax a smaller value, but both well above that of air. An approximate expression for capacitance is $C = 9kA/t$, where C is in picofarads, k is the permeability (unity for air and up to 20 or so for other materials), A the area in square metres for each plate (both assumed to be equal), and *t* is the spacing between the plates in metres.

Radio-tuning capacitors and some small trimmers use air dielectric. Other variable capacitors may use mica or similar dielectric, while many small fixed capacitors use paper, plastic film (polyester capacitors), mica or ceramic material as the dielectric. The required capacitance value is achieved by rolling into a cylinder the dielectric and the metal foil forming the plates, as shown in Figure 6.10. This technique, of course,

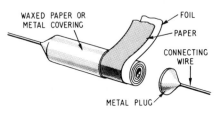

Figure 6.10. Construction of 'rolled up' tubular capacitor

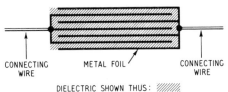

Figure 6.11. Mica 'sandwich' type capacitor, sometimes called 'silver mica' (see also (a) in Figure 6.12)

results in plates of large effective surface area. Smaller-value capacitors are sometimes constructed after the style shown in Figure 6.11. A typical small capacitor of mica dielectric of this construction is shown in Figure 6.12(a).

Other designs include polyester-foil construction, where the plastic dielectric is 'silvered' or consists of a thin conductive foil, and ceramic construction, examples being shown in Figure 6.12(b) and (c).

152

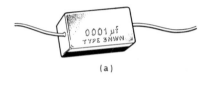

(a)

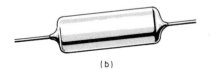

(b)

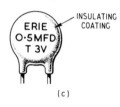

INSULATING
COATING

ERIE
0·5MFD
T 3V

(c)

Figure 6.12. Types of fixed capacitor:
(a) silver mica, (b) polyester, and (c)
ceramic

Variable capacitors

A common variable capacitor is that used for tuning (see also
Chapter 5), and a two-gang capacitor of this kind is shown in
Figure 6.13(a); its circuit symbol is shown at (c). This uses air
dielectric and consists of sets of intermeshing (but not
touching) plates, one set of each gang fixed and the other set
rotatable by means of the tuning control, which is commonly
a slow-motion mechanical arrangement that also operates
the cursor over the tuning scales. As the fixed and variable
plates come more into mesh, so the capacitance increases.

153

The plates are often specially shaped to provide the required tuning law – that is, the capacitance change per increment of rotation.

An earlier design of variable capacitor is shown in Figure 6.13(b). Again fixed and variable plates are used, but here mica instead of air is used as the dielectric.

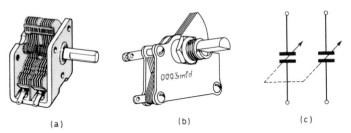

Figure 6.13. Variable capacitors: (a) air dielectric, (b) mica dielectric; (c) circuit symbol for two-gang type

Variable capacitors have maximum values up to 800 pF or so, down to a few picofarads with the plates fully out of mesh (this due to the inherent or self-capacitance).

Varicaps

Tuning is also nowadays achieved by capacitor-diodes, or *varicaps* as they are often called. Each tuned circuit includes a single diode whose capacitance varies as the reverse bias across it is adjusted by a potentiometer, thereby tuning the circuit. See also Chapters 5 and 7.

Trimmers

Trimmers and preset capacitors, too, have air or solid material as the dielectric; examples (with the circuit symbol) are shown in Figure 6.14. They are used to *trim* and *pad* the tuned circuits so that the correct range of frequencies is covered by the main tuning control, so that all the circuits tune in step while holding the i.f. difference at the local oscillator (see Chapter 5), and so that all the stations appear at the corresponding frequency or wavelength points on the tuning scale. A trimmer is connected in parallel with the main

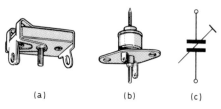

(a)   (b)   (c)

Figure 6.14. Examples of trimmer capacitors: (a) compression type with mica as the dielectric; (b) threaded type with air as the dielectric; (c) circuit symbol

tuning capacitor, while a padder usually appears in series with the resonant circuit. A trimmer tracks the high frequencies and a padder the low frequencies, the adjustments being made together for the best overall tracking.

Electrolytic capacitors

Electrolytic capacitors permit the development of large capacitances in relatively small dimensions. This is achieved by a very thin dielectric being formed by a chemical layer between the plates. The dielectric-forming process is based on a jelly electrolyte (early electrolytics employed liquid, and were called 'wet' electrolytics), rather like the electrolyte of an electric cell. The electrolyte surrounds the first plate, upon which is formed a very thin layer of oxide (aluminium oxide when the plate is of aluminium) owing to the action of the electrolyte. This layer, which is the dielectric, becomes stronger when the capacitor is in circuit and subjected to a voltage. The second plate consists of the electrolyte itself, since this is spread evenly over the oxide-coated side of the first plate. Connection to the electrolyte, which is conductive, is often made to the outer metal case of the capacitor or to a second non-coated electrode.

The electrolytic capacitor needs to be connected to the voltage in the correct polarity to instigate the chemical action. If it is connected the wrong way round a high leakage current flows, and the dielectric disappears; the capacitor then overheats and might ultimately explode!

After a period of inactivity, the dielectric weakens, and to avoid high leakage current it is desirable to reform the dielectric by starting with a low voltage and gradually working up to the capacitor's working voltage. The electrolytics in radio equipment that has not been used for some time are best reformed by connecting the equipment to the supply via a Variac transformer, which allows the voltage to be increased gradually as the dielectric is reforming.

Electrolytic capacitors have values going up to thousands of microfarads, but the higher-value ones generally have lower working voltages than smaller-value ones; the former are designed for relatively low-voltage transistor circuit applications, going up to tens of volts, and the latter for high-voltage smoothing and decoupling applications, going up to hundreds of volts, depending on physical size (small, high-value electrolytic capacitors are generally of low working voltage).

In recent years various categories of low-voltage electrolytic capacitors have been developed to meet the requirements of transistor circuits, including the solid-electrolyte tantalum capacitor and printed-circuit-board configurations. Although based on the principles just described, some of the new electrolytics employ different manufacturing techniques and materials.

Working voltage

An electrolytic must always be selected for a working voltage close to that of the voltage in the circuit. If the circuit voltage is low compared with the working voltage, incorrect dielectric forming will result and the leakage current may rise. Conversely, too high a circuit voltage for the capacitor will cause overheating, internal gassing and ultimate failure.

Non-polarised electrolytics

So-called non-polarised electrolytics are also available, and are used in such things as loudspeaker frequency-dividers. Some varieties of tantalum capacitor are of this kind; an alternative arrangement is a common-can encapsulation of two polarised electrolytics connected in series positive-to-positive or negative-to-positive or negative-to-negative. The total capacitance is reduced by this method, as we have seen, so that if each capacitor is, say, $4\,\mu F$, the total capacitance would be $2\,\mu F$. It sometimes pays to connect high-value resistors in parallel with the capacitors when so connected (e.g. a $1\,M\Omega$ across each capacitor) for equalisation.

Electrolytics are also avalable as multiple units, such that one encapsulation contains two or more capacitors with terminations for each one, the negative side being common to all the capacitors.

Ripple rating

Electrolytics used for power-supply smoothing should have a suitable ripple current rating; that is, the capacitor should be able to accommodate the a.c. component of the d.c. without overheating.

Power factor

This refers to the loss in a capacitor, and is defined as the cosine of the phase angle times VI, as already explained. The power factor of good-quality non-electrolytic capacitors can be as small as 0.01 (at $1\,kHz$). Power loss in electrolytic capacitors, however, is generally larger, up to about 0.4,

157

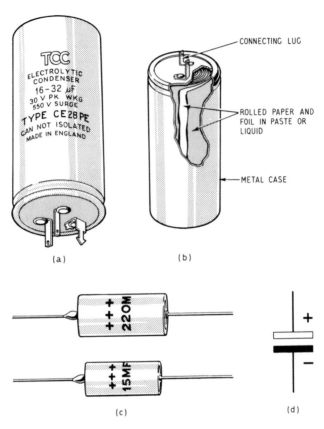

Figure 6.15. Examples of electrolytic capacitors: (a) two-unit can type; (b) inside construction; (c) tantalum capacitors; (d) the electrolytic capacitor symbol

depending on type, value and working voltage. Power factor indicates how much power is consumed by the capacitor in heating the losses.

Some examples of electrolytics are shown in Figure 6.15 along with the symbol of the component. Non-electrolytics and electrolytics of various types can also be seen in the photos of Figures 6.6 and 6.7.

Capacitors in series and parallel

Capacitors connected in series provide a total capacitance equal to a value whose reciprocal is equal to the reciprocal of the sum of the reciprocals of each capacitor in series, such as $1/C_t = 1/C1 + 1/C2 + 1/C3$ ... etc, similar to *parallel*-connected resistors. When connected in parallel, however, the values of all the capacitors are added together (e.g. $C_t = C1 + C2 + C3$ ... etc) similar to *series*-connected resistors.

Inductors

As explained in Chapter 1, the flow of current through a conductor produces a magnetic field, and the reaction of this back into the conductor is called *inductance*. When the conductor takes the form of a coil of wire the field intensity is increased, as also is the inductance. Further increase occurs

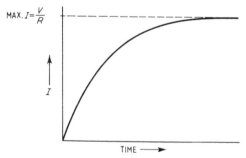

Figure 6.16. When a voltage is applied across an inductor the current does not rise immediately to its $I = V/R$ value as with a resistor, but develops exponentially with time owing to the back e.m.f. combating the applied voltage (see text)

when a core of magnetic material is placed in the coil. A component possessing inductance is called an *inductor*.

When a voltage is applied across a pure resistor there is an almost instantaneous flow of current of magnitude $I = V/R$.

159

When a voltage is applied across an inductor the current increases *gradually*, ultimately limited by the d.c. resistance of the winding and the value of the voltage ($I = V/R$ again). The current build-up with time, as shown in Figure 6.16, stems from the changing magnetic field cutting the turns of wire. The e.m.f. so generated in the winding is in opposition to the applied voltage, and since this tends to force the current to flow in the opposite direction to that due to the applied voltage, there is a gradual, exponential build-up of current.

The unit of inductance is the henry (H). When an opposing or back e.m.f. of 1 V results from a rate of change of current of 1 A per second, the self-inductance of the component is 1 H. Note that it is the change of current divided by the time period of the change. Thus, if a change of, say 0.1 A occurred in 0.1 second, the inductance would still be 1 H.

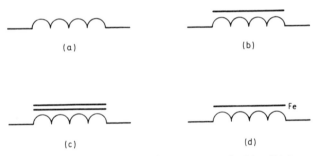

Figure 6.17. Inductance symbols: (a) air-cored, (b) solid iron-cored, (c) laminated iron-cored, (d) ferrite-cored

The energy stored by an inductor is $\frac{1}{2}LI^2$ joules, where L is in henries and I in amperes.

Some inductor symbols are given in Figure 6.17. Only the large components used for power supply and audio frequencies have values in the henry region, and these are the iron-cored variety with many turns of wire. As with capacitors, sub-multiples are used, giving the millihenry (mH = 10^{-3} H) and the microhenry (μH = 10^{-6}H).

A typical application of a large-value component (10H or so) is for smoothing rectified (see Chapter 7) mains supplies, large-value electrolytic capacitors also being used in the filter circuit, as shown in Figure 6.18. In this application the inductor is sometimes called a *choke* (smoothing choke), and such a component is shown in Figure 6.19, the symbol of which is that in Figure 6.17(b) or (c).

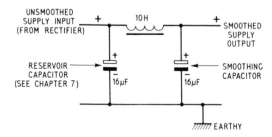

Figure 6.18. Showing the use of a 10H choke in a smoothing filter

Figure 6.19. L.F. smoothing choke, 10H value (see Figure 6.18)

Chokes of lower inductance value are also used in r.f. circuits to 'block' radio-frequency signals from power-supply circuits, for example. These have the make-up shown in Figure 6.20, where (a) is air-cored and (b) and (c) are ferrite-cored, having the symbols shown in Figure 6.17(a) and (d) respectively.

When a.c. is applied to an inductor the current is equal to V/X_L, where X_L is the inductive reactance equal to $2\pi fL$ (*f* the frequency in hertz and *L* the inductance in henries). As we

161

noted in Chapter 5, the expression reveals that X_L rises in direct proportion to the inductance and the frequency (it will be recalled that capacitive reactance X_c has an *inverse* relationship). Thus, while the reactance of an inductor increases with frequency, that of a capacitor decreases with frequency. It is this property that makes an inductor a good 'isolator' of unwanted signals. The d.c. is limited merely by the resistance of the winding, while the a.c. is neatly blocked or 'choked'.

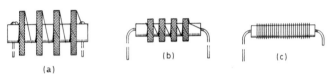

Figure 6.20. Examples of r.f. chokes: (a) air-cored; (b) ferrite-cored; (c) small-inductance ferrite cored

A capacitor, on the other hand, makes a useful component for signal coupling because the d.c. isolation is very good and the signal coupling impedance low, depending on value and frequency.

Because initially the voltage is maximum and the current minimum, the voltage across an inductor is a quarter of a cycle (90 degrees) in front of the current through it when the input is a.c. In other words, the current *lags* the voltage by 90 degrees (remember that the opposite situation occurs with the capacitor). The *phase angle*, as it is called, is 90 degrees only when the capacitor is loss-free. In a practical world there is never absolute perfection, so the phase angle of practical capacitors is less than 90 degrees, but only slightly so when the resistance of the winding is small. Resistive losses are minimised by using copper wire of the largest practical diameter.

Magnetic losses are kept small by good core design, while eddy-current losses (those resulting from the action of the conducting core material) are minimised by the cores of the large-value components (for power and audio frequencies) being composed of laminated sections insulated from each other, and the cores of the smaller-value r.f. components being composed of ferrite (iron particles suspended in an insulating material).

Owing to the 90-degree current/voltage phase displacement, the power loss in a pure inductance is zero (as in a pure capacitance). The power loss or power factor is given by the cosine of the phase angle, which is zero at 90 degrees and unity at zero degrees. The phase angle is given by $\tan^{-1} X_L/R$, where X_L is the pure reactance and R the resistive losses. Thus if at a particular frequency X_L is, say, 8 ohms and R is 1 ohm, the phase angle is $\tan^{-1} 8/1$, or pretty well 83 degrees, and the power factor is 0.12, signifying a 12 per cent resistive power loss.

The term r.f. (radio frequency) can be attached to all chokes and inductors used for this sort of application in radio receivers and associated circuits; but an indication of the part of the spectrum for which a component is particularly designed is sometimes given by the terms h.f., v.h.f. and u.h.f. – applied to inductances with values of the order of millihenries, microhenries, and fractions of a microhenry, respectively, though these should be regarded only as a rough guide.

Tuning coils

A tuning coil is merely an inductor of a value selected to resonate with a capacitor to provide the required tuned frequency (or range of frequencies when the capacitor is variable). As explained in Chapter 5, the resonance frequency (f_0) of an inductor/capacitor combination is that frequency where $X_L = X_c$, or $f_0 = 1/2\pi\sqrt{(LC)}$, where f is in hertz, L in henries and C in farads.

Tuning coils are made so that the inductance value provides the required tuning frequency (the windings on intermediate-frequency transformers, for example) or range of frequencies when used in conjunction with a specific-value (fixed) capacitor, trimmer or variable capacitor. Tuning coils for the a.m. bands generally have several windings, or a tapped winding, that can be switched to provide the inductances for the several wavebands. Sometimes separate l.w., m.w. and s.w. coils are used. A coil is needed for each tuned circuit, of course.

For padding purposes, the coils often include adjustable ferrite cores. These adjust the inductance values, and facilitate the tracking (ensuring that all the circuits tune in step) at the low-frequency ends of the bands. The use of low-resistance wire, sometimes of special design, and ferrite cores keeps the losses low, which is the requirement for a high Q value and hence good selectivity (see Chapter 5).

Ferrite cores increase the inductance, which thus *decreases* as the core is screwed *out* of the winding. Brass cores have the opposite effect; that is, the inductance is *decreased* as the core is screwed *in*.

Coils for tuning the u.h.f. and v.h.f. bands are of very low inductance, having only a few turns of wire; they are sometimes air-cored. They may also be tapped (a tapping connected along the winding) for back coupling (oscillators) and matching. Coils for the short wavebands are of a higher inductance and thus use more turns, while medium and long waveband coils have even higher inductance, and more turns, particularly the l.w. coils.

Transformers

The transformer effect has already been briefly discussed (Chapter 1). When two windings are placed in a common magnetic circuit and an alternating voltage applied across one winding, an alternating voltage appears across the second winding, owing to the changing magnetic field produced by the energised winding. The winding across which the voltage is applied is called the *primary* and the winding across which the voltage appears is called the *secondary*. Although there is usually only one primary winding, there can be more than one secondary winding, depending on the purpose for which the transformer is designed.

In a perfect, loss-free transformer the ratio of the input/output voltages V_{in}/V_{out} is the same as the primary/secondary turns ratio N_p/N_s, i.e. $V_{in}/V_{out} = N_p/N_s$. The ratio of the currents, however, equals the *inverse* turns ratio, i.e. $I_{in}/I_{out} = N_s/N_p$. Although the voltage or the current can be stepped up, there is no *power* gain. In fact, there is a loss since there is no such thing as a perfect transformer. The loss, though, is usually small, and a well designed transformer has a good efficiency.

A transformer can thus be used to convert the a.c. mains to a low-voltage power supply or to transfer a signal from one circuit to another. Since the windings can be separate and of good isolating resistance, a transformer can be used to isolate, from the d.c. point of view, one circuit from another. Moreover, in the case of a mains transformer, the primary can be heavily insulated also from the metal core of the transformer and the latter bonded to a good earth. By this scheme, which is adopted by some radio receivers and hi-fi amplifiers, the user is protected from electric shock in the event of the transformer insulation failing.

Impedance matching

A transformer can also be used as an impedance-matching device. For example, if it is required to match a 50-ohm microphone to an amplifier input of, say, $10\,k\Omega$, a transformer can be interposed between the two. The impedance ratio is equal to the square of the turns ratio, i.e. $N_1^2/N_2^2 = Z_1/Z_2$, so substituting the values for Z we have, in this case, $N_1^2/N_2^2 = 10\,000/50$, i.e. $N_1/N_2 = \sqrt{200}$, which works out to 14.14; this means that the secondary in this case must have 14.14 times more turns than the primary.

Transformer symbols are shown in Figure 6.21. That at (a) is of a mains transformer employing a tapped primary and three secondaries, one of which is tapped. When the correct mains input is applied across the primary, the turns ratio of the transformer is so designed that the required voltages appear across the secondaries. The tappings on the primary allow adjustment of the turns ratio to suit slightly different mains voltages.

The symbol at (b) could be an audio coupling transformer or loudspeaker transformer. A laminated iron core is signified by two solid lines between the windings. The

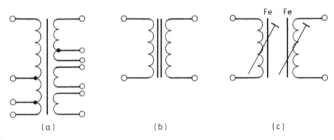

(a)   (b)   (c)

Figure 6.21. Transformer symbols: (a) mains transformer with tapped primary and three secondaries, one tapped; (b) microphone, loudspeaker, coupling, etc. transformer; (c) r.f. transformer with ferrite cores that are adjustable

symbol at (c) indicates a transformer using ferrite cores which, as signified by the diagonal lines with 'T' ends, are adjustable. This sort of transformer would most likely be involved with higher frequencies, such as radio and intermediate frequencies; but transformers with similar cores are used in other applications, such as in the stereo decoders of hi-fi receivers.

Autotransformer

There is no need for a transformer to have two (or more) *isolated* windings. The transformer effect results also from any inductor with a tapping, as shown in Figure 6.22. Although this resembles a resistive potential-divider, the output is much steadier over a range of current drawn than it is with a resistive divider. This is because of the transformer action resulting from the full winding (primary) and the part winding (secondary).

Known as an *autotransformer*, this component also exhibits the impedance-transforming property of its brothers with separate windings, and the property is commonly exploited in coupling one r.f. stage to another for maximum energy transference. The same rules apply, the main difference being the lack of isolation. To provide a variable source of alternating voltage, the tapping is sometimes made in the form of an adjustable wiper which, when operated by a control knob, represents the well known *Variac* transformer.

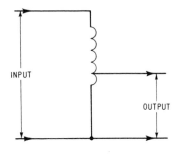

INPUT

OUTPUT

Figure 6.22. Basic autotransformer (see text)

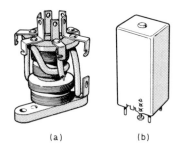

(a)   (b)

Figure 6.23. (a) R.F. transformer, (b) i.f. transformer in can

Power and audio transformers use laminated cores to reduce eddy-current losses. R.F. transformers use ferrite cores (and so-called pot cores, enclosing the whole of the winding), as their inductor counterparts.

An r.f. transformer is shown in Figure 6.23(a). That at (b) is an i.f. transformer in a metal case, which prevents unwanted coupling to other parts of the circuit.

Signal inversion

Another property of a transformer is that of signal inversion. For example, the signals at the two terminals of the secondary, relative to a common terminal (centre-tap, say), are effective 'mirror images' of one another, as shown in Figure 6.24. This property is sometimes exploited for 'push-pull' driving of amplifier valves.

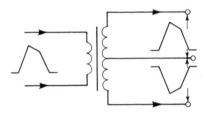

Figure 6.24. Signal inversion effect of transformer

Mutual inductance

When one winding is coupled to another, as in a transformer, there is a *mutual inductance* (M) of 1 H between the two when an e.m.f. of 1 V is induced across the secondary owing to a 1 A per second current change through the primary. If the total inductance of the two windings is measured when they are connected so that the turns of the two are running the same way (L_s), and then again when the turns of one winding are running in the opposite direction to those of the other (L_0), then: $M = (L_s - L_0)/4$.

This expression is derived from: $L_s = L_1 + L_2 + 2M$ and $L_0 = L_1 + L_2 - 2M$, where L_1 and L_2 are the individual inductances of the two windings.

As we have seen, unwanted coupling between different coils is avoided at r.f. by screening. With r.f. transformers, of course, the coupling is deliberate, but the transformer as a whole is then often screened.

Inductors in series add as the sum and in parallel as the reciprocal sum of the individual inductance values assuming zero mutual inductance, the same formula as resistors.

Tuned and coupled windings

With tuned and coupled windings, as the r.f. transformer shown in Figure 6.23, the overall response curve is altered by the degree of coupling between the two windings. When the coupling is *loose* and the two circuits are resonated to the same frequency the response curve tends to peak as shown at (a) in Figure 5.18 and, as already noted, the bandwidth is reduced from that of just a single tuned circuit (see Chapter 5). As the coupling is increased so the output from primary to secondary increases to a maximum and the top of the response curve flattens, producing a response curve similar to that shown at (b) in Figure 5.18. At the optimum point of this 'flatness' the coupling is said to be *critical*, and this occurs when the coupling between the two windings is $1/Q$ of the inductance of either winding.

Further increase of coupling from critical, or *tight* coupling as it is called, results in the centre-top of the response curve dimpling downwards, producing what is commonly known as *double-hump* tuning. Over-critical coupling is rarely used for ordinary r.f. transformers, though to extend the bandwidth while retaining sharply-falling side-skirts, an approximation of this sort of coupling may be used along with a circuit having a more peaky type of response characteristic to fill in the top dimple.

R.f. transformers often have fixed coupling, the two windings being cemented onto a common former, though various methods are adopted in the r.f. or i.f. transformers used in communications receivers to provide variable inductive coupling. Selectivity is nowadays also enhanced by the use of ceramic and quartz piezoelectric crystals. Such a crystal represents a very high Q-factor resonance circuit (see Chapters 4 and 9).

The coefficient of coupling (k) of two circuits is given by $M/\sqrt{(L_1 \times L_2)}$ and the mutual inductance (M) is related to k by: $k\sqrt{(L_1 \times L_2)}$, where k equals 1 for 100 per cent coupling. The coefficient of coupling is also equal to $1/\sqrt{(Q_1 \times Q_2)}$, where Q_1 and Q_2 are the respective Q factors of the two windings (e.g. $Q = 2\pi fL/r$ – see 'Magnification factor' in Chapter 5).

169

Transmission line

Apart from being used for coupling signal from an aerial to a receiver or from a transmitter to an aerial, transmission line can also be used for impedance transformation. Most of us know that transmission line can be either coaxial cable or twin, the former unbalanced feeder being most common from the FM radio (and TV) point of view. Open balanced feeder (two parallel wires held apart by spacers) is used mostly by the radio amateur fraternity and possible short-wave listeners.

Now, if we have an infinite length of transmission line and apply a short pulse to the input, this will continue travelling along the line, getting weaker and weaker as it goes owing to resistive losses. At this stage it is worth noting that the speed a radio signal travels down transmission line is less than that at which a radio signal travels through space. Chapter 2 has told us that through space a radio signal travels at 300 metres per millionth of a second (μs). Through feeder it may only be 60 to 80 per cent of this speed. This is a function of the so-called *velocity factor* of the line which generally ranges from about 0.6 to 0.8, depending on the nature of the line.

Anyway, let's now cut the line to make it a finite length and short the end across. Sending down the pulse again it will be reflected at the short and return up the line to the launching point. If instead of a short we put a resistor across the line and adjust its value, we will find a value where the pulse will be completely absorbed and not reflected back up the line. The resistor value so discovered would have the same value as the *characteristic impedance* of the line (Z_0).

When the line is so terminated, the other end of it will also show a value of Z_0. This is just what we aim to do when coupling an FM radio, for instance, to an aerial through feeder cable. Coaxial transmission line for this purpose generally has a Z_0 around 75 ohms, and both the aerial-input circuit of the receiver and the feed impedance of the aerial are designed to have a similar impedance. When this state of affairs exists the system is properly matched and the coupling efficiency is maximum.

A transmission line contains distributed inductance along its length and distributed capacitance between its conductors, with the inevitable resistive losses. Excluding the losses, Z_0 is given by $\sqrt{(L/C)}$, where L is the inductance in henries and C the capacitance in farads.

When a finite length of line is not terminated, the end shorted *or* open-circuit, the input impedance swings widely as the frequency is changed. When the line is made a quarter wavelength of the operating frequency, taking account of the velocity factor, a short-circuit one end gives a high impedance the other end, an open-circuit one end gives a low impedance the other end, while if one end is terminated with a resistor equal to Z_0 the other end will also show an impedance equal to the value of the resistor.

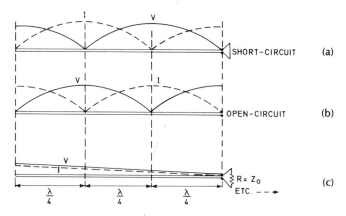

Figure 6.25. Showing the voltage and current distribution over quarter-wave lengths of line, (a) with end short-circuited, (b) with end open-circuit and (c) with end matched to Z_0

This quarter-wave effect of transmission line is commonly exploited for matching purposes. Figure 6.25 shows the voltage and current distribution and the standing waves which result from non-matching, the latter having much in common with the standing waves of a half-wave dipole aerial (Chapter 3).

171

One application of a quarter-wave line is that if, say, your FM radio is being interfered with by a very strong local signal outside Band 2, say at 144 MHz, then by cutting the line to the quarter-wave of 144 MHz, taking account of the velocity factor, and connecting this in parallel with the aerial feeder at the receiver end, leaving the other end open-circuit, the interfering signal would be effectively 'short-circuited' by the low impedance of the line at that frequency, leaving the required Band 2 signals substantially unaffected. Let's suppose the velocity factor is 0.6, then the line would approximate $(300 \times 0.6)/(144 \times 4)$ or 0.312 m in length. It would be best to make it a little longer and then trim it down a small bit at a time until the best interference rejection is achieved.

Another interesting application is that, if you wanted to connect two Yagi aerials for stacking or baying to a common feeder, you could use a quarter-wave line for matching. Each aerial would be connected to 75-ohm feeder, each of the same length, and when these two are connected in parallel the impedance would drop to 37.5 ohms. The problem, then, is to match that impedance to the 75-ohm main down feeder. The solution is to connect a quarter wave-length of coaxial feeder of calculated Z_0 between the main feeder and the junction of the other two going to the aerials.

The formula for working out the Z_0 is: $\sqrt{(Z_{in} \times Z_{out})}$ where Z_{in} is the input impedance (37.5 ohms) and Z_{out} the output impedance (75 ohms). Working the little sum out with these figures comes to a value of 53 ohms, so you would settle for 50-ohm coaxial for the quarter-wave line.

Quarter-wave transforming line is useful for a whole range of applications, and now that you have the general idea I expect you will be able to work out some of your own!

7

Valves, solid-state devices and transistors

Most contemporary radio and amplification equipment uses transistors and integrated circuits as the active components. Transistors are looked at later in this chapter and integrated circuits in Chapter 8. The components considered in Chapter 6 can be regarded as *passive* because they do not themselves contribute to the power in the circuits – indeed, they reduce it. It is the job of the *active* components to make good the loss of power and to provide a net power gain – for example, to amplify a weak input signal so that its voltage and/or current and hence its power is greater at the output than at the input.

Diode valve

In some forms the valve is an active component; but in its basic guise it is fundamentally a rectifier (i.e. converts a.c. to d.c.), and is called a *diode* owing to its use of two electrodes, called the *cathode* and *anode*. These are suitably spaced, the anode surrounding the cathode, in a glass envelope from which much of the air has been evacuated. The temperature of the cathode is raised by passing an electric current through a small coil of 'resistance' wire, called the *heater*, which causes the cathode to emit electrons into the vaccum. If a positive potential relative to the cathode is then applied to the anode, the emitted electrons are attracted to the anode and current flows through the valve.

A vacuum is necessary for the action because without it the electrons would collide with the much larger molecules of the gas and little or no electron current would flow. Moreover, the heater would soon burn out, as would the filament of an electric light bulb that was cracked and hence 'down to air'.

Some valves employ just a heater which acts also as the cathode, the term *filament* then being more appropriate. However, an indirectly heated cathode facilitates the use of an a.c. heater supply. Some valves with filaments (directly heated cathodes) require a d.c. supply.

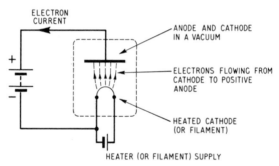

Figure 7.1. The diode valve. The electrodes are contained within an evacuated glass envelope, and the electrons (current carriers) liberated by the heated cathode (or filament) are attracted to the positive anode. With the anode negative there is no flow of electrons through the valve and hence no conduction. The diode thus passes current in one direction only

From this basic description it will be appreciated that the electrons flow from cathode to anode only when the anode is more positive than the cathode (see Figure 7.1). When the anode is made more negative than the cathode the electrons return to the cathode and there is no current flow through the valve. In other words, the valve (as implied by its name) is a one-way device.

Principle of rectification

The valve thus makes a very good rectifier, because it passes only the negative or positive half-cycles of an a.c. waveform, as shown in Figure 7.2. Some valves designed specifically for rectification employ two anodes, and are called full-wave rectifiers. A valve in such a circuit is given in Figure 7.3. Here

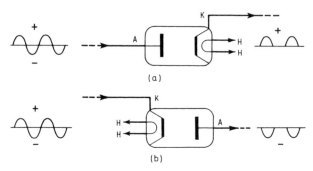

Figure 7.2. The diode valve as a rectifier. The positive or negative half-cycles of input signal appear at the output depending on which way round the diode is connected

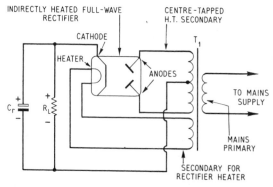

Figure 7.3. A double-diode valve in a full-wave rectifier circuit. Valves of this kind are designed specifically for power rectification but are now mostly superseded by semiconductor diodes.

a mains transformer (see Chapter 6) with a centre-tapped secondary applies alternate positive and negative half-cycles to the two anodes, relative to the centre-tap. Thus one anode conducts on one half-cycle and the second anode on the other half-cycle, so that both half-cycles are rectified.

In this case, however, for a given d.c. output the mains transformer secondary needs to supply two times the a.c. input of the single-diode circuit, e.g. 250–0–250 V as opposed to just 250 V for the same output single-diode arrangement.

With single-diode rectification, called appropriately half-wave rectification, the ripple or unidirection d.c. at the output has a frequency equal to that of the supply frequency. Thus, if 50 Hz mains is being rectified, the ripple is also at 50 Hz, as illustrated at (i) in Figure 7.4(a). With a full-wave rectifier the output ripple is twice the input frequency, or 100 Hz on a 50 Hz mains supply, as illustrated at (ii) in Figure 7.4(a).

It is also possible to obtain full-wave rectification from a single (non-tapped) input by using four diodes in a bridge circuit. Semiconductor diodes are now commonly used in this sort of circuit, as shown on page 193.

Filter circuits at the output of the rectifier (see Figure 6.18) eliminate the ripple component to produce pure d.c. from the rectified a.c. supply. The higher the ripple frequency, the smaller can be made the values of the filter components for a given degree of smoothing, which is one reason why full-wave rectification is preferred in low-hum-level equipment.

Going back to Figure 7.3, the smaller secondary on the transformer energises the heater of the rectifier, and it is not uncommon to find additional low-voltage secondaries for the heaters of the other valves. Resistor R_L represents the load which, in practice, is formed by the circuits being powered. Electrolytic C_r is the *reservoir capacitor* which, in the absence of load current, charges to the peak value of the input waveform. C_r charge is topped up during each rectifier 'pulse', the capacitor then supplying current to the load during the intervals between the 'pulses'. Thus, the amount by which C_r voltage falls from peak during each discharge

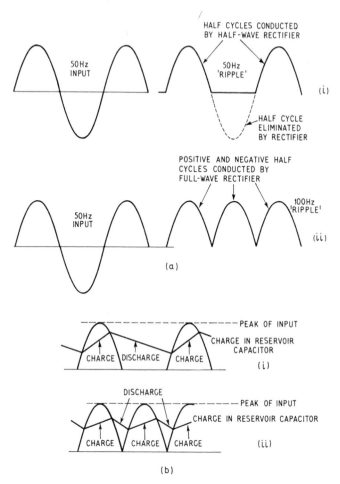

Figure 7.4. (a) Half-wave rectification yields output 'pulses' at input frequency rate (i), while full-wave rectification yields pulses at twice the input frequency rate (ii). (b) The reservoir capacitor charges during the 'pulses' and discharges by supplying current to the load during the intervals between the pulses. With full-wave rectification (ii), the charge is topped up twice as frequency as with half-wave rectification (i), which allows the reservoir capacitor to have a smaller value for full-wave than for half-wave rectification for a given ripple output and load current (see text)

cycle depends on the value of C_r and on the frequency of the 'pulses'. Figure 7.4(b) shows the effect relative to half-wave rectification at (i) and to full-wave rectification at (ii).

The result is a 'triangular' type of ripple of average value equal to the d.c. The ripple is attenuated by passing the output from C_r through an RC or LC filter. The filter shown by Figure 6.18 is an LC type. Since the inductor or choke has a fairly low resistance to d.c. and a high impedance to a.c., the d.c. is allowed to pass but the ripple is attenuated. The subsequent smoothing electrolytic further attenuates the ripple. In some circuits where the load current is not too high, a resistor is used in place of the inductor or choke; the ripple then developed across the series resistor is bypassed by the following capacitor. The principle outlined is common to all rectifying circuits, irrespective of frequency of input supply (or signal) and type of rectifier (valve or solid-state). The filter has the characteristics of a low-pass filter.

Peak inverse voltage

The diode (or diodes) is stressed by a voltage across it in excess of the peak of the a.c. input. Consider a half-wave rectifier without its load. On the conducting half-cycle the reservoir charges to the peak value of the a.c. input which, say, on 100 V is close to 141 V (e.g. peak $V = \sqrt{2}$ of V_{input} r.m.s.) This will hold one side of the rectifier at that potential while during the non-conducting half-cycle the peak voltage will also be 141 V but of the opposite polarity at the other side of the rectifier. Voltage across the rectifier will thus be 2×141, or 282 V. This is called the *peak inverse voltage* (p.i.v.). To provide a fair margin the rectifier should have a p.i.v. rating some 12 to 15 per cent higher. The p.i.v. rating is particularly applicable to semiconductor rectifiers.

A fair approximation to the requirements is obtained as the product of π and the d.c. output voltage of half- and full-wave (one and two diode) circuits and the product of $\pi/2$ and the d.c. output voltage for bridge rectifier circuits, which use four diodes (see page 193).

Mean diode current is equal to the d.c. output of half-wave rectifier circuits and to half the d.c. in the case of two-diode and four-diode bridge circuits.

Triode valve

A simple diode valve is not designed for signal amplification. For this it is necessary to control the electron flow, and hence current, from cathode to anode. This is achieved by interposing a third electrode between the cathode and anode. This, called the *grid*, is of a grid- or mesh-like structure that does little in the physical sense to hinder the flow of electrons from cathode to anode – they merely pass through it. However, when a negative potential is applied to it, it then significantly influences the electron flow. If it is made substantially negative with respect to the cathode, the electrons emitted by the cathode are repelled and they then return to the cathode, thereby cutting off the electron flow to the anode. A less negative potential causes some of the electrons to pass through the mesh of the grid to the anode, the result being a reduction in anode current (I_a). Thus by adjusting the negative potential on the grid it is possible to control the current flowing through the valve, from zero to the maximum established by the anode voltage (V_a) and the design of the valve.

As would be expected, with a fixed grid voltage (V_g) it is possible to change I_a by adjusting V_a, but the amount of variation that can be achieved by this means is very limited. For example, while a change of less than 1 V at the grid could change I_a by 10 mA or more, it might need a change in V_a of 200 V or more to obtain a similar (10 mA) I_a change. The change in I_a resulting from a change in V_g, expressed in mA/V, is called the *mutual conductance* (g_m). For example, to say that a triode has a g_m value of 10 mA/V means that a 10 mA change in I_a occurs from a 1 V change in V_g. Mutual conductance is an example of a *parameter*.

Another parameter is the *slope resistance* (R_a), which is the change in V_a resulting from a change in I_a (or in cathode current), the result generally being expressed in kilohms. The product $g_m R_a$ of a triode is the *amplification factor* (μ) which means that the voltage amplification is proportional to the mutual conductance and load resistance: the higher these are, the higher the amplification.

The basic triode-valve circuit, showing the triode symbol and some of the factors discussed, is given in Figure 7.5, while the 'characteristic curves' of a triode valve, also showing the amplification effect, are given in Figure 7.6.

Triode amplifier

Amplification results from the small change in voltage at the grid producing a much greater change in voltage across a load resistor (R_L) connected in series with the anode and the high-tension (h.t.) supply voltage, the latter stemming from the change in I_a. Provided the grid is *biased* negatively, the input signal applied to the grid causes a relatively linear I_a swing, which is converted to signal voltage swing across R_L. Under this condition the grid takes virtually no current, which means that the input impedance is very high, usually being established by a grid resistor in the circuit. The grid bias is generally adjusted (for class A amplification) to the centre, most linear, part of the I_a/V_g characteristic, as shown in Figure 7.6. Provided the input signal does not swing the grid to a positive value (which would result in grid current) and the output does not exceed the I_a limit of the valve and supply, the output signal across the load is a fair, increased-voltage replica of the input signal, but of opposite phase.

Biasing

A triode amplifier is shown in Figure 7.7. When the valve is conducting, current flows through R_L and R_k (the cathode resistor), which makes the cathode positive with respect to the negative line. Since the grid is connected to the negative

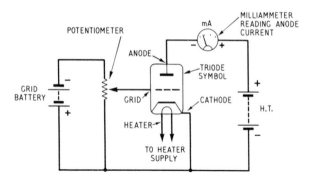

Figure 7.5. Basic circuit of triode valve, showing symbol. As the negative voltage at the grid is increased by the potentiometer, so the anode-current reading on the milliammeter falls

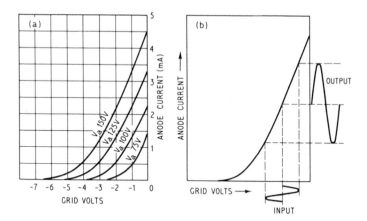

Figure 7.6. Characteristic curves of a triode valve. (a) Curves for four different anode voltages (V_a); while a 1 mA change in I_a results from a 25 V change in V_a, the same I_a change occurs from a meter 1 V change in V_g. (b) A small signal input voltage at the grid causes a larger current swing at the anode; the signal current through the anode load resistor produces a voltage across the load of greater amplitude than that at the grid, thereby providing voltage amplification

line through the grid resistor R_g, the grid becomes negative with respect to the cathode, thereby neatly providing the grid bias of a value set by R_k.

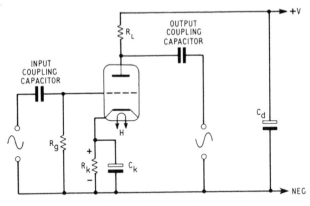

Figure 7.7. Triode-valve amplifier circuit (see text)

Signal-wise, capacitor C_d puts the top of R_L to the negative line since it has a low X_c at the signal frequencies. The signal across R_L is thus relative to the negative line, and it is fed out through the output coupling capacitor, which isolates the d.c. and leaves only the a.c. or signal. The input signal to the grid is likewise isolated, both capacitors being chosen for a suitably low X_c over the operating frequency range of the amplifier. The R_a of the valve is effectively in series with R_L, and if the valve is regarded as a generator of $V = \mu V_g$ it can be understood that R_a and R_L form a potential-divider from which the output signal is tapped, as shown in Figure 7.8. The caption of Figure 6.5 gives the appropriate expression, and using this in conjunction with the $V = \mu V_g$ generator we get the expression:

$$\text{Signal out} = \mu V_g \; \frac{R_L}{R_a + R_L}$$

There are other factors that need to be taken into account by the circuit designer, including such things as the

182

grid-to-cathode input capacitance and the anode-to-grid capacitance. The latter is called the *Miller-effect capacitance*, and is responsible for feedback.

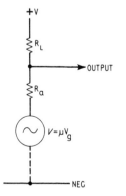

Figure 7.8. The valve can be re-garded as generator of $V = \mu V_g$, with R_a as the source resistance. With the anode load resistor R_L a potential-divider is formed so that the output signal is equal to $V = \mu V_g \times R_L/(R_a + R_L)$ (see also Figure 6.5)

In Figure 7.7, the cathode capacitor C_k bypasses the signal voltage that develops across R_k. Without this decoupling, signal would get back to the grid (in the same way as the bias is derived), antiphase with the input signal, and would reduce the gain owing to negative feedback.

Tetrode and pentode valves

The main disadvantages of the triode are the fall-off in gain with increasing frequency, owing to the anode/grid capacitance, and the comparatively low available amplification resulting from the relatively small R_a of the triode. The anode/grid capacitance is also an embarrassment in r.f. circuits, because when the input and output couplings are tuned circuits the capacitance encourages positive feedback (from anode back to grid) and hence sustained oscillation.

The interposition of a fourth electrode (also of a grid-like structure through which the electrons can pass) between the grid and anode overcame the internal capacitance problem, and because of the now four electrodes the valve was named *tetrode*. The first grid then became known as the *control grid* and the second as the *screen grid*. To combat the grid/anode capacitance the screen grid needs to be made 'earthy' from the signal's point of view, so is connected to the 'earthy' side of the circuit through a capacitor. To keep the electrons flowing through, the valve also needs to be connected to a positive potential, which is through a resistor (or direct) to the positive h.t. supply line.

The screen grid also has the added advantage of increasing the valve's R_a and hence its amplification factor; but it has the disadvantage of attracting secondary electrons, which fly off the anode due to its bombardment by the electrons of the main stream. This puts a 'kink' on the characteristic curve, which under certain conditions can distort the signal or give rise to oscillation.

This problem was resolved by the interposition of a third grid between the screen grid and anode; by making this the same potential as the cathode the secondary electrons are suppressed. This third grid is thus called the *suppressor grid*. In some circuits, such as mixers, modulators, etc., the suppressor grid is made an active element.

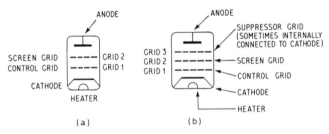

Figure 7.9. The symbols of the tetrode and pentode valves

The five-electrode valve is called a *pentode*, and its symbol and that of the tetrode are given in Figure 7.9. Note that the grids of a valve are commonly referred to by number in order of placement outwards from the cathode. Thus in a pentode the control grid is G1, the screen grid G2 and the suppressor grid G3.

Owing to the pentode's high R_a, its control grid has a greater influence on I_a than that of the triode. The suppressor

184

grid also reduces further the control-grid/anode capacitance. With a pentode the total cathode current is more dependent on the screen-grid voltage than the anode voltage, and when cathode biasing is used (see Figure 7.7) the voltage developed across R_k is proportional to the sum of I_a and the screen-grid current.

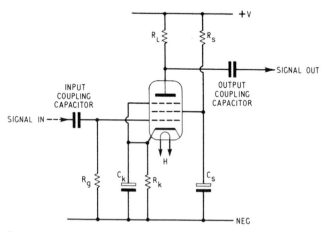

Figure 7.10. Circuit of pentode amplifier stage, where R_g is the control-grid load resistor, R_k the cathode resistor, C_k the cathode capacitor, R_L the anode load resistor, R_s the screen-grid resistor and C_s the screen-grid decoupling capacitor. Grid bias results from the voltage across R_k due to the sum of I_a and I_{sg}, while C_s puts the screen grid to the 'earthy' potential from the signal's point of view. C_k decouples the signal across R_k and thus prevents degenerative or negative feedback

Also owing to the high R_a of the pentode, a change in V_a has little effect on I_a, which is tantamount to the pentode being a current generator of $g_m V_g$ mA, i.e. controlled by V_g. In conjunction with a high R_L, therefore, pentodes are capable of high amplification, and before the advent of the transistor they were commonly used as voltage amplifiers in audio equipment and as small-signal amplifiers in r.f. and i.f. stages of radio receivers. A typical pentode amplifier stage is shown in Figure 7.10.

185

Other valves

A valve popular with amplifier designers prior to the take-over by the transistor was the beam-power tetrode. Instead of the suppressor grid of the pentode, this valve uses specially shaped plates (internally connected to the cathode) to guide or beam the electrons to the anode. Such valves are still found in the push-pull power amplifier stages of earlier hi-fi amplifiers, and at the time of writing there is an indication that a mild revival in this area is occurring!

During the valve heyday a wide variety of valves for specific applications were developed, including such multiple valves as double-triodes, triode-pentodes, double-diode-triodes, triode-hexodes, triode-heptodes, etc. Hexodes (six electrodes), heptodes (seven electrodes) and octodes (eight electrodes) are species designed essentially for signal-mixing and frequency-changing applications. Some of these are becoming increasingly more difficult to obtain for replacement purposes. Heater- or filament-voltage and current ratings were engineered to suit the diversity of requirements of the day.

Although valved radios are no longer being made commercially, there must be quite a few of them still in service. Today's designs are all based on so-called solidstate electronics using semiconductors in various guises, such as the transistor, integrated circuit, junction diode and so forth. However, valves are still used in the power amplifier (p.a.) stages of amateur transmitters.

Semiconductors

As would be expected, a *semiconductor* is a material possessing a limited number of current carriers – it is neither a good conductor nor a good insulator. Specially prepared semiconducting materials are used in the various solid-state devices, the required degree and nature of the conductivity being achieved by the controlled introduction of impurities, which yield the current carriers. This is called *doping*.

The basic semiconductor material is crystal, two common types being germanium and silicon. In pure state and at normal temperature these possess very few current carriers and are thus good insulators. Figure 7.11 shows the crystal lattice of germanium (symbol Ge). Each atom has four electrons, and lattice bonding results from inter-atom linking by the electrons. These are called *valence electrons*, as distinct from the 'free electrons' of a conducting material.

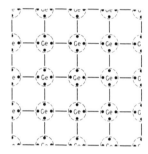

Figure 7.11. The crystal lattice of germanium (Ge)

At normal temperature germanium is an almost perfect insulator, but as the temperature is increased so valence electrons are encouraged by thermal energy to depart from the lattice (i.e. the germanium is *ionised*); they are then available for current carrying, which is not a particularly good thing. The same applies to silicon, but this crystal requires a higher temperature for release of valence electrons. For correct working, therefore, semiconductors must not be permitted to get too hot, and 'heat sinks', forced air and other artifices are adopted to keep the crystal temperature of power-handling semiconductors reasonably low.

To impart semiconducting properties to the basic crystal closely controlled impurity atoms are introduced. These do not alter the original nature of the lattice, but they release current carriers into the crystal, thereby increasing its conductivity.

N- and p-type semiconductors

Such an impurity is antimony or arsenic, an atom of which is called *penta*valent because it is equipped with *five* valence electrons. Four of these bond each impurity atom into the crystal, and the remaining one is available for current carrying. This sort of semiconductor is called *n-type*, 'n' indicating negative or electron carriers.

Another impurity employed is aluminium or indium, an atom of which is called *tri*valent because it is equipped with *three* valence electrons. While atoms of such material merge with the basic lattice, the electron spaces are not all filled, there being an electron vacancy for each impurity atom in the crystal lattice. Quite logically, an electron vacancy is called a *hole*, and as would be expected a hole exerts an attractive force on an electron, which means that it can be regarded as a positive charge or positive current carrier. This sort of semiconductor is called *p-type*, 'p' indicating positive current carriers.

When an electron is release from, say, a germanium atom in p-type semiconductor by a rise in temperature or by any other effect (such as light or electric field), it is attracted to and eventually captured by a hole. The hole the electron leaves behind has the same attractive influence on another free electron in the material. Thus when electrons are passed into p-type semiconductor they move in one direction, filling up the holes as they go, and leaving other holes in their wake; the holes thus move in the opposite direction to the electrons.

In summary, then, controlled quantities of electrons, called negative current carriers, are present in n-type semiconductor, while holes, called positive current carriers, are present in p-type semiconductor. The carriers are caused to move and thus conduct electric current by subjecting the semiconductor to an electric potential.

The atoms of impurity are called *donors* for n-type and *acceptors* for p-type, and they can ionise like any other atom; acceptors then develop a negative charge by losing a positive hole, and donors develop a positive charge by losing a negative electron. Ionisation is precipitated by heat, as already noted, which results in an increase in current and hence more heat, ultimately giving way to a condition called *thermal runaway*, with consequent damage to the crystal.

188

Light, too, can encourage ionisation and thus affect the current flow.

Semiconductor diode

For use in diodes and transistors, the two types of semiconductor are integrated during the processing of the crystal so that one side is a p-type zone and the other side n-type. The meeting point of the two zones is called the *junction*. There are various ways by which this processing is carried out, and the method used is sometimes indicated by the name given to the device. One way involves the crystallisation of originally molten p-type semiconductor on to n-type semiconductor. Another way is by *diffusion*, where one type of semiconductor is 'spread' into the other by heating. There is also the *epitaxy* method, where the vapour of one type is caused to condense on the other type.

POTENTIAL BARRIER
AT JUNCTION

Figure 7.12. The development of the 'potential barrier' at a pn junction interface

The initial effect of such integration is a flow of electrons from the n-type into the p-type and a flow of holes from the p-type into the n-type across the junction. After this initial carrier interchange the n-type interface of the junction becomes positivity charged owing to loss of electrons, while the p-type interface becomes negatively charged owing to loss of holes. These two charges form a 'potential barrier' across the junction interface so that further interchange of carriers is halted; the idea is shown in Figure 7.12.

Figure 7.13 shows how a semiconductor junction of this type acts as a rectifier. At (a) an external potential connected as shown *reinforces* the inherent potential barrier, which makes it even more difficult for current to flow across the junction. Here the junction is said to be in *reverse bias*, and the only current that flows within the rating of the device is that due to minority carriers, which is very small.

At (b) the external potential is reversed, the junction then being said to be in *forward conduction* or *forward bias*. This allows the interchange of large numbers of carriers across the

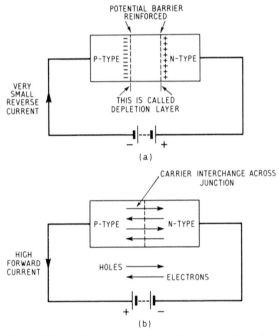

Figure 7.13. (a) The 'potential barrier' is reinforced when a pn junction is connected in reverse bias, there then being little or no current flow. (b) When connected for forward conduction there is free carrier interchange across the junction and hence easy current flow

junction and hence a large flow of current through the device, depending on its current and power ratings. Small junctions can pass milliamperes of current, large junctions (particularly when heat-sinked) many amperes of current when in forward conduction. Rectification efficiency is high and the output resistance relatively low, because of the very high reverse resistance or impedance and the very low forward resistance or impedance. Such simple junctions are called *junction diodes* – analogous to the two-electrode diode valve.

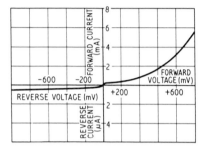

Figure 7.14. Reverse and forward characteristics of small junction diode. Note that the forward current is in milliamperes and the reverse current in microamperes

Another type of semiconductor diode is the *point contact* type. This uses a semiconductor upon which contact is made by a springly tungsten wire fused to the surface of the semiconductor by a small region of opposite-type semiconductor. The point contact diode is a latter-day version of the early crystal detector, years ago found in crystal sets. Since a diode rectifies, of course, it will also demodulate a radio signal as shown in Chapter 5.

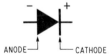

Figure 7.15. Semiconductor diode (rectifier) symbol

Figure 7.14 shows the reverse and forward characteristics of a small junction diode, and Figure 7.15 gives the semiconductor diode symbol. The arrow side corresponds to the anode and the straight line to the cathode. Forward current flows when the anode is positive with respect to the cathode; the arrow thus indicates the direction of conventional current flow, not electron flow.

Semiconductor junctions (including those in transistors – see later) have specific parameters related to their application. Some of the important ones are:

(i)   *peak reverse voltage*, which is the maximum voltage in the non-conducting direction that can be applied – important for power rectifiers, for example;

(ii) *maximum forward current*, which is the conducting current, sometimes given as a peak value, dictated by temperature and hence heat-sinking in the larger devices;

(iii) *voltage drop*, which is indicative of the power loss in the device under conducting conditions;

(iv) *charge storage*, which is the time it takes for the current carriers (electrons and holes) to 'stabilise' after a switching operation, and is thus an indication of switching speed.

Bridge rectifier

Power diodes capable of handling a large current and having adequate p.i.v. characteristics are now commonly used in bridge rectifier circuits instead of the earlier thermionic valve. As mentioned at the beginning of this chapter this sort of circuit provides full-wave rectification from a single input source. A typical circuit is given in Figure 7.16(a).

Voltage doubler

Semiconductor diodes can also be easily arranged to double the voltage from a single a.c. voltage input, the basis of such a circuit being given in Figure 7.16(b).

What happens is that on the positive half cycle D1 conducts and charges the reservoir capacitor to the peak value of the a.c. input, at this time D2 being non-conducting. On the

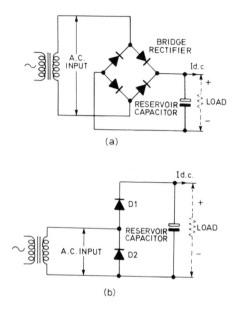

(a)

(b)

Figure 7.16. Bridge rectifier circuit using semiconductor diodes. This provides full-wave rectification, the ripple output being 100 Hz from a 50 Hz mains supply (a). The diagram at (b) shows how two semiconductor diodes can be arranged to provide voltage doubling from a single source input

negative half cycle D2 conducts and D1 switches off so that the peak voltage across the reservoir then becomes the peak of the a.c. input *plus* the voltage to which the capacitor has already charged. The effect then, of course, being a d.c. output twice the voltage obtained from an ordinary rectifier circuit.

Other diodes (capacitor-diode)

In addition to the basic semiconductor diode, numerous specialised diodes have evolved over the years. An interesting one is the so-called capacitor-diode or *varicap*, which is used for f.m. and, more recently, a.m. tuning (see also

Chapters 5 and 6). As shown in Figure 7.13(a), a *depletion layer* occurs in proximity to the junction when a junction diode is reverse-biased. This gives rise to capacitance across the leadout wires of the diode, the value of which decreases with increase in reverse bias (as shown in Figure 7.17) owing to the widening of the depletion layer. Owing to the small

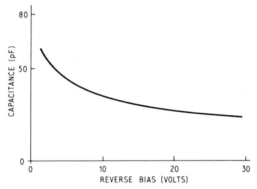

Figure 7.17. The capacitance across a varicap decreases as the reverse bias increases. This results from the widening of the depletion layer – see Figure 7.13(a)

reverse conduction, the loss of the so-formed capacitance is very small. The circuit section in Figure 7.18 shows how such a diode is used in a tuned circuit. Each tuned circuit has its own diode (sometimes two connected back-to-back, to combat non-linearity), and all are adjusted in capacitance together by the common potentiometer. Recent varicaps have a greater capacitance swing than the earlier species, which makes them suitable also for a.m. tuning, where a greater capacitance range than for f.m. tuning is needed.

Zener diode

Another diode found in radio circuits for power-supply regulation is the zener diode. In the forward direction this sort of diode has a fairly normal characteristic. In the reverse

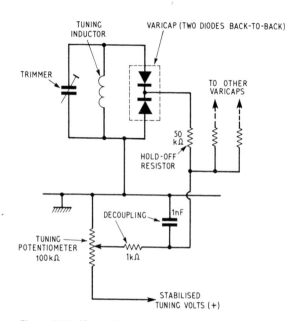

Figure 7.18. The varicap is connected across the tuning coil (inductor) and the reverse bias is adjusted by the tuning potentiometer, whose input voltage is stabilised to avoid tuning drift. Initial setting of the tuned circuit is accomplished by the trimmer capacitor. Each varicap may consist of a single diode or of two diodes connected back-to-back, the latter (as shown) tending to counter non-linearity

direction, however, the current starts very low until a certain voltage is reached, called the *zener voltage*. At this point the reverse current rises swiftly and a large current change causes only a small change in voltage across the diode. This is shown at (a) in Figure 7.19. The effect is exploited for voltage regulation, as shown at (b). Provided the value for R is chosen so that the diode operates in the zener region at the lowest input voltage, then the output voltage will remain substantially constant regardless of change in input voltage. The output voltage is delivered at the low resistance of the diode,

195

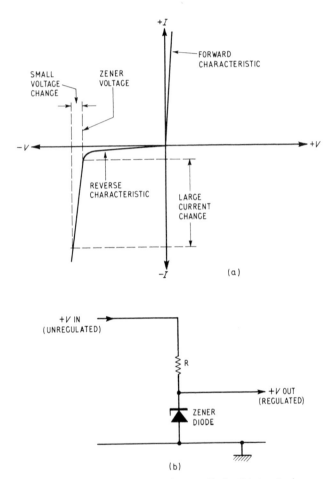

Figure 7.19. (a) Characteristics of zener diode; (b) circuit of zener diode regulator, showing zener diode symbol (see text)

called the *dynamic resistance*, which is equal to the voltage divided by the current in the zener region. For example, if a change of 0.02 A (20 mA) results in a change of 0.1 V (100 mV), then the dynamic resistance is a mere 5 ohms, which is very good. This sort of regulation is sometimes used for the tuning voltage of varicaps. Notice the zener diode symbol in Figure 7.19(b).

More potent voltage and current regulation can be achieved with transistors whose voltage reference is commonly produced by a zener diode.

There are many other diodes found in electronics, including the avalanche diode, tunnel diode, Shockley diode, Gunn diode, photo diode, etc., but most of these have applications outside ordinary radio-receiver techniques.

Bipolar transistor

The basic *bipolar* transistor is an integration of two semiconductor diodes. A *pnp* transistor has n-type semiconductor sandwiched between two p-type semiconductors,

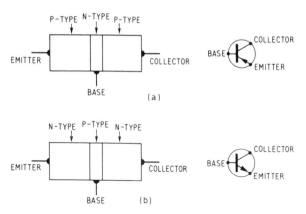

Figure 7.20. Elementary impressions of (a) pnp and (b) npn transistors, with their symbols

while an *npn* version has the p-type semiconductor as the 'meat' of the sandwich. Two junctions are thus formed in both cases, as shown at (a) and (b) in Figure 7.20, along with the appropriate symbols. The junctions are developed in

197

manufacture in a similar way to the junction of a diode. However, because the middle semiconducting region is extremely thin the diode actions interact to yield the transistor effect.

The middle semiconductor is called the *base* and the two outer regions the *emitter* and *collector*. When a transistor is used as an amplifier, the emitter – base junction is biased for forward conduction and the collector – base junction for reverse conduction. Thus, relative to emitter, the base and collector of a pnp transistor are connected to negative volts, while the base and emitter of an npn transistor are connected to positive volts.

Considering a pnp transistor so biased, holes pass across the emitter – base junction because of the forward bias and, owing to the thinness of the base region, diffuse through the sandwiched semiconductor, thereby entering the collector region. The negative volts here strongly attract the holes, causing current to flow into the collector, which gives rise to collector current (I_c).

While holes are diffusing through the base region some combine with the base electrons, but many get through to the collector, and the narrower the base region the less the hole loss.

I_c is thus governed by the quantity of holes passing across the emitter – base junction, and since the quantity depends on the forward current across this junction it follows that I_c will increase with increase in base current (I_b). When I_b is switched off, therefore, I_c collapses, and any current measured here will be that of minority carriers (i.e. *reverse leakage current*).

The npn transistor works similarly, except that this time *electrons* diffuse through the base region and come under the attractive force of the positive collector to give I_c.

The important point to note is that a large I_c (flowing between emitter and collector) results from a much smaller I_b (flowing between emitter and base), thereby yielding *current amplification*. The various voltages and currents applicable to pnp and npn transistors are indicated respectively at (a) and (b) in Figure 7.21.

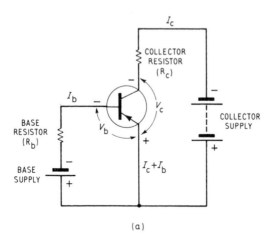

(a)

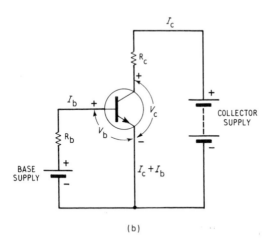

(b)

Figure 7.21. Voltages and currents associated with bipolar transistors: (a) pnp and (b) npn

An amplifying stage based on an npn transistor is given in Figure 7.22 where, as is usual, there is just the single power supply, the emitter – base voltage (V_{eb}) being obtained from the voltage-divider R_1/R_2. The collector load is R_3, while R_4 in the emitter circuit tends to combat thermal runaway by reducing V_{eb}. For example, should the current rise the voltage across R_4 will also rise so that the emitter goes more positive with respect to the base. In other words, the base goes less positive with respect to the emitter so that I_b is reduced and with it I_c.

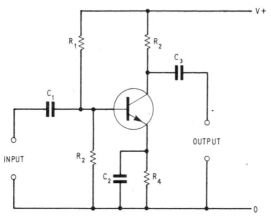

Figure 7.22. Circuit of signal-voltage amplifier stage based on an npn bipolar transistor (see text)

Signal is coupled in through C_1 and out through C_3, while C_2 across the emitter resistor puts the emitter to the common 'earthy' point so far as signal is concerned, thereby avoiding degenerative (negative) feedback and hence gain reduction.

A circuit based on a pnp transistor would be virtually the same except, of course, for the polarity of the power supply, which would be the other way round. This basic circuit is used for many applications (including r.f. and i.f. ones) where the collector load is formed by a tuned circuit or tuned coupling to the base input of the following stage. The values of the components, too, are selected for the application in hand. The circuit in Figure 7.22 is often referred to as a *common-emitter* stage, since the emitter is common to both input and output. It has moderately high input and output impedances, depending on the values of the components.

Two other configurations are *common-base*, where the base is made common to input and output, the input being applied to the emitter and the output taken from the collector, and *common-collector* (or *emitter-follower*), where the collector is made the common electrode, the input being applied to the base and the output taken from the emitter. The first mentioned has a low input impedance and high output impedance, and the second a high input impedance and low output impedance. Such stages are often used as 'buffers' and impedance-matching circuits.

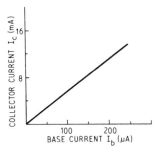

Figure 7.23. Transfer characteristic of bipolar transistor in common-emitter mode. This expresses the current amplification factor

The various parameters of the transistor are listed in the author's book *Servicing Radio, Hi-Fi and TV Equipment* (Newnes Technical Books). A primary one is *current gain*, signified by beta (β) or h_{FE}, which indicates the amount of I_c change for a change in I_b, given as a ratio. For example, if I_c changes by 14 mA when I_b is changed by 0.25 mA (250 μA), the h_{FE} would be 14/0.25, or 56. Transistors of much higher current gain than this are available. Figure 7.23 gives the common-emitter transfer characteristic of a transistor, which shows the current gain or *current amplification factor* as it is sometimes called. There are hosts of other characteristics, and readers wishing to delve more deeply into the theory of transistors have a wide range of literature available from which to study.

It will be appreciated, of course, that the transistor also amplifies signal voltage (indeed, the circuit in Figure 7.22 is that of a signal-voltage amplifier). This is because the voltage developed across the collector load resistor, due to the I_c swing, is far greater than that developed across the base resistor from input-signal swing. Also, because power is the product of current and voltage, a transistor provides power gain, gains in the order of 2000 times (33 dB) not being uncommon.

When amplifying a.f., i.f. and r.f. signals, other factors come into play, such as capacitances between the electrodes, RC coupling components, transformers, etc.

For audio power amplification a *push-pull* pair of transistors is commonly used, with each one of the pair being biased for almost I_c cut-off. This means that in the absence of drive signal the current taken by the pair is very small, and is called *quiescent current*. As the drive is increased so the transistors conduct alternately on the positive and negative half-cycle of the signal, the total current then increasing well above the quiescent value, depending on the drive amplitude and signal power delivered.

For small-signal stages a single transistor is used and is biased to the middle of its characteristic. This is called class A working. When a transistor is biased to I_c cut-off and then driven as described, this is called class B working. When the biasing is for a small quiescent current (required to reduce certain types of distortion), this is referred to as quasi-class B working or class AB working. Hi-fi amplifiers are of the latter class.

Large power transistors are mounted on heat-sinks for cooling, but the smaller ones are commonly supported on their leadout wires.

Field-effect transistor

A bipolar transistor is so called because it exploits two types of current carriers: electrons *and* holes. The field-effect transistor (f.e.t.) uses only one type of carrier, depending on its polarity (n-channel or p-channel), electrons *or* holes. There are two basic types, *junction gate* and *insulated gate*. As with the bipolar transistor, there are basically three electrodes, the *gate* which controls the device, like the grid of a valve or the base of a bipolar transistor, the *source* which is akin to the valve cathode or the bipolar-transistor emitter, and the *drain* whose analogue is the valve anode or bipolar-transistor collector. Symbols of the various types are given in Figure 7.24.

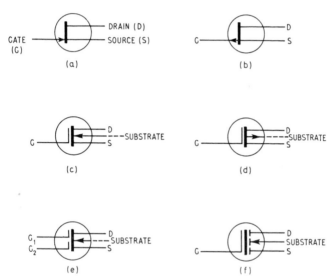

Figure 7.24. Symbols of field-effect transistors: (a) junction-gate n-channel, (b) junction-gate p-channel, (c) insulated-gate depletion n-channel, (d) insulated-gate depletion p-channel, (e) insulated-dual-gate depletion p-channel, and (f) insulated-gate enhancement n-channel

An n-channel junction-gate f.e.t. consists of a strip of n-type semiconductor which, in conjunction with a centre section of p-type semiconductor, is styled into the form of a very narrow channel through which the current carriers flow. One end of the n-type strip is the source and the other end the drain. The centre p-type section is the gate, which

203

controls the carrier flow. Since the gate of an f.e.t. in this polarity is negative with respect to the source, the centre pn junction is in *reverse* bias. Its impedance is thus high.

Under zero-bias conditions the n-channel conductivity is high and electrons flow relatively unhindered through the channel from source to drain. As the reverse bias is increased, however, so the flow of electrons is inhibited, the source-to-drain current thus falling; when the bias is further raised conduction eventually ceases, the channel then being 'pinched off'.

A p-channel junction-gate f.e.t. works similarly, but since the current carriers are holes the potential is reversed.

The insulated-gate f.e.t. has an even higher gate impedance than the junction-gate type. This is because the gate is effectively insulated from the conduction channel by a very thin layer of oxide, the abbreviation m.o.s.t. (metal oxide semiconductor transistor) or m.o.s.f.e.t. (metal oxide silicon field effect transistor) signifying this type of device.

The conduction channel (n-channel types) is formed between two regions of n-type semiconductor placed either side of a piece of p-type semiconductor. The gate is placed across the two n-type regions and insulated from them by the oxide. The n-type regions form the source and drain. Biasing in one mode is such that both drain and gate are made positive with respect to the source, electrons in the n-type source then being attracted by the positive gate. Electrons are thus drawn into the channel between the source and drain, and are attracted by the latter since this is positive. The quantity of electrons in the channel therefore depends on the number attracted by the electrostatic charge of the gate (bearing in mind that this is insulated). This type of f.e.t. is called *enhancement* because the drain current (I_d) is increased or enhanced by the gate bias. Its basic construction is shown in Figure 7.25.

Another version is called *depletion* because I_d falls with increase in gate bias, though it will rise when the bias is increased in the opposite polarity. The biasing of an f.e.t. is thus governed by its type, the circuit, of course, taking this into account. M.O.S.F.E.T.s are also made with two gates.

This construction makes it possible for the input signal to be applied to one gate, and a control voltage or a signal to be 'mixed' to the other gate, with a high degree of isolation. For example, when a dual-gate f.e.t. is used as an r.f. amplifier, the signal to be amplified is applied to one gate, while the other gate can be used for gain control by the application of a bias potential – i.e. automatic gain control (a.g.c.) When used as a mixer or frequency changer, the second gate can be used for the application of the local-oscillator signal. If the substrate is not connected to a separate leadout wire, it is internally connected to source.

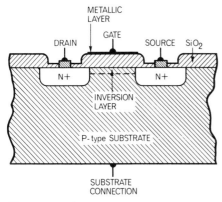

Figure 7.25. Elementary impression of the make-up of a metal oxide silicon field-effect transistor

The f.e.t. also serves very effectively for switching operations, though in radio receivers it is mostly found as a signal amplifier or mixer. It is essentially a small-signal device, but a recent development (in Japan) has lifted it to the realm of power amplification, hi-fi amplifiers now being available with push-pull power f.e.t. output stages.

Owing to the high (often extremely high) gate input impedance (resulting from the reverse-biased gate junction or the oxide insulated gate) an f.e.t. is often regarded as being voltage operated, like the thermionic valve, as distinct

205

from the current (base) control of a bipolar transistor. The transfer characteristic of an f.e.t., too, tends to have more in common with that of a thermionic valve than does the characteristic of a bipolar transistor. The characteristic of an f.e.t. is essentially square-law, rather like that of a triode valve, which means that it performs admirably as a low-noise mixer. Such a characteristic also reduces third-harmonic components, which makes the f.e.t. particularly useful for applications like r.f. amplifiers, where there is a requirement for low cross-modulation and intermodulation products. The f.e.t. is thus often found in the r.f. amplifier and mixer stages of f.m. tuners and receivers. It is also being used more for audio preamplification.

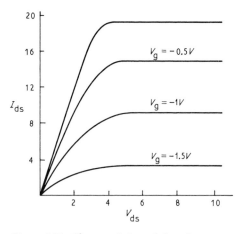

Figure 7.26. Characteristics of junction-gate f.e.t. (see text)

The characteristics of a junction-gate f.e.t., drain/source current (I_{ds}) being plotted against drain/source voltage (V_{ds}) with the gate voltage (V_g) as parameter, are shown in Figure 7.26. These reveal that V_g has a greater influence on I_{ds} than has V_{ds}. The characteristics in this respect, therefore, are very much like those of a pentode valve of high slope resistance.

8

Integrated circuits

In addition to transistors and semiconductor devices of various types, the contemporary radio receiver is often equipped with integrated circuits (i.c.s). The manufacture of an i.c. follows the basic techniques evolved for that of a transistor; that is, photo-etching and vacuum evaporation processes are employed. An i.c., in fact, consists of a multiplicity of transistors and semiconductor junctions

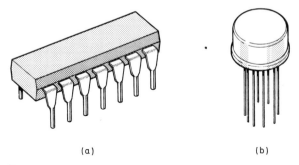

(a)   (b)

Figure 8.1. I.C. encapsulations: (a) dual-in-line and (b) multilead TO-99

formed on a single chip of silicon, along with the required interconnections. The chip is about the same size as that which would be used for a single transistor, but the encapsulation is generally larger to cater for a greater number of lead-out and lead-in conductors associated with the various elements.

There are several encapsulations; those often found in radio receivers and hi-fi equipment include the dual-in-line, the single-in-line and the multilead in a TO-5 or TO-99 encapsulation, which is similar to, though larger than, a transistor encapsulation. All, of course, are designed for printed-circuit board attachment.

The first i.c.s were essentially for the field of digital electronics, and were designed for operating at only two voltage or current levels, coded 1 and 0 in accordance with the binary system. Digital i.c.s are used extensively in counting, computer and calculator electronics.

Most of the i.c.s found in radio receivers, however, are *linear*, i.e. the amplitude of the output signal changes proportionally with the amplitude of the input signal. Owing to the cascading of a number of stages, a single linear i.c. can have an astonishingly high signal gain, and such an i.c. is termed an *operational amplifier* (op-amp for short). The stages are fully or partly interconnected, and the lead-in and lead-out wires from and to the various elements facilitate the introduction of external (discrete) components and hence the development of circuit sections for specific require-ments. Some of the i.c.s found in certain parts of television and hi-fi receivers combine linear and digital functions.

Because the elements inside i.c. op-amps are all coupled directly together (no coupling capacitances) they are capable of amplifying d.c. as well as a.c. In radio circuits, however, we are concerned mostly with the amplification of 'signals' (a.c.). In this case the d.c. component is deliberately blocked by coupling capacitances external to the i.c. op-amps. Amplification of d.c. is sometimes required for control functions (such as tuning meter indication, automatic gain control (a.g.c.), etc.) and in these cases the coupling capacitors are omitted.

I.C. symbols and schematic diagrams

Schematic diagrams of i.c.s are not usually included in the circuit diagrams of the equipment employing them. To do so would make the circuits far too complicated. Instead, the i.c. op-amps are represented by arrowheads or blocks, as shown at (a) and (b) in Figure 8.2; the former is the more common symbol for op-amps, while the latter is used for all types of i.c.s. The block of the more complicated species may be divided into smaller sections and marked to signify the

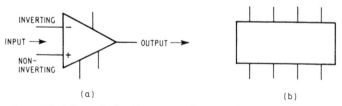

Figure 8.2. I.C. symbols: (a) op-amp; (b) general

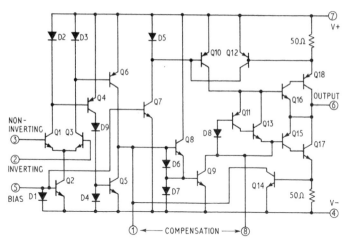

Figure 8.3. Schematic diagram of RCA CA3078T/AT i.c. operational amplifier (see text)

various functions yielded by the device in the particular circuit. Schematics, however, are supplied by the device manufacturers, and an example is given in Figure 8.3; this is a diagram of the RCA CA3078T/AT, which is an i.c. op-amp designed for particularly low standby power consumption.

As in most op-amps, there are two inputs, marked non-inverting and inverting, the first going to the base of Q_1 and the second to the base of Q_3. The Q_1/Q_3 configuration is called a *balanced long-tail pair*, and a number of such pairs are found in i.c.s. Transistor Q_2 along with diode D_1 provides a constant-current source for the tail. Transistors and diodes provide balanced stablisation against temperature and voltage changes, while *Darlington pairs* (i.e. Q_{11}/Q_{13}) are used as drivers. Output is delivered by the fully complementary output stage comprising Q_{15}/Q_{16} and Q_{17}/Q_{18}.

Some i.c. op-amps include resistive elements, while capacitance is sometimes introduced by semiconductor junctions in reverse bias (see Chapter 7). To maintain stability it is sometimes necessary to apply external compensating capacitance, and the terminals in Figure 8.3 designated 'compensation' are for this purpose. To avoid damage to the output transistors in the event of a short-circuit at the output when the i.c. is being driven, many of the latest devices include short-circuit protection.

For instrument applications and other applications where a high input impedance is required, i.c. op-amps are available with field-effect-transistor input stages. However, the input impedance is also dependent on the way in which the i.c. is used, particularly with regard to the nature of the feedback.

I.C. op-amp parameters

The gain of an i.c. op-amp without feedback, called the *open-loop gain*, can be very high; for example, the i.c. shown in Figure 8.3 has a gain of 100 dB (100 000 times the voltage). To tailor an i.c. for a specific application the gain is deliberately reduced by negative feedback, which also reduces the distortion and increases the bandwidth. The gain then resulting is called the *closed loop gain*. The *frequency response* of an i.c. op-amp, like that of a transistor, is governed by the design and the inhertent capacitances within the elements and circuits. As a general rule, the frequency response is quoted as that frequency where the voltage gain falls to unity, the gain then rising at a rate of 20 dB/decade with reducing frequency, as shown in Figure 8.4.

Gain falling with frequency at the rate of 20 dB/decade is not very useful for signal amplification. The requirement for this application, of course, is for a constant gain over the frequency bandwidth of interest; this is achieved by the use of negative feedback, which provides the lower closed-loop gain up to the high-frequency limit imposed by the device itself, as shown by the broken-line characteristic in Figure 8.4. Here the closed-loop gain holds at 20 dB (10 times the

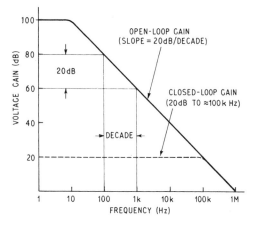

Figure 8.4. In the open-circuit mode the gain of an i.c. op-amp falls with increasing frequency at the rate of 20 dB/decade, as shown. A constant gain over a required frequency range is achieved by the use of negative feedback, which gives the closed-loop gain, as shown by the broken-line characteristic

voltage) from d.c. (0 Hz) to around 100 kHz. At that frequency the feedback runs out and the h.f. limitation of the device itself starts to take over. If a higher closed-loop gain is required, then less feedback is applied; but this causes the gain to start to fall from its higher value at a lower frequency.

High gain allied with extended frequency response calls for a high-gain i.c. op-amp of inherently wide frequency response.

Frequency response is a *small-signal* parameter. The h.f. output of large amplitude is limited by the i.c.'s *slewing rate*, which refers to the maximum peak output voltage available at a given high frequency at the onset of serious signal distortion. The highest frequency to the point of serious distortion at a given peak output voltage can be discovered from the simple expression.

$$f = SR \times 10^6 / E_p 2\pi$$

where SR is the slewing rate in V/μs and E_p is the peak output voltage within the capability of the i.c. The frequency is given in hertz. Thus, while an i.c. may have a small-signal response to 100 kHz or more and an output capability of ±10 V (meaning 20 V peak-to-peak or 10 V peak), if it has a slewing rate of only 1 V/μs the highest frequency that it would accommodate at 10 V peak without distortion would be less than $1 \times 10^6/10 \times 6.28$, i.e. 15 923 Hz (15.923 kHz).

In other words, the slewing rate limits the ultimate output-voltage swing at high frequencies referred to waveform distortion. It should be understood that the slewing-rate limiting is a function of the i.c. op-amp itself and is not changed by negative feedback. It implies that the amplifier is incapable of delivering further current to continue charging the capacitance associated with the load.

Input bias current is another parameter of i.c. op-amps, and refers to the current that must be fed to the input to bring the output voltage to zero. As in a transistor, such biasing is necessary to secure linear amplification; but with i.c.s its value is often very small – a mere 7 nA for the CA3078T/AT.

Input offset voltage is another parameter to be found or i.c. op-amp specification sheets. It is the direct voltage that needs to be applied across the input pins to bring the output voltage to zero. The effect is different from the biasing, since it serves to 'balance' the i.c. Some i.c.s include pins for connecting a variable resistor for offset adjustment.

212

Common-mode rejection ratio. Owing to the non-inverting and inverting inputs, a spurious signal arriving together at the two inputs will tend towards cancellation within the i.c. The common-mode rejection ratio indicates the degree of rejection afforded to such signals in this common mode.

Other parameters include such things as *rise time* (how long it takes the output signal to rise from 10 per cent to 90 per cent of its maximum value when the input is a step function; in the small-signal sense, rise time is associated with frequency response), *settling time* (how long it takes the output signal to settle after a step function), *output voltage swing* (maximum output voltage obtainable without waveform clipping with zero quiescent current), etc. It is clearly impossible to define all the parameters in the compass of this present book; but students requiring more detailed information will not find a dearth of literature on the subject of i.c.s.

I.C. op-amps applications

In many applications i.c. op-amps are arranged in feedback configurations, basic examples of which are given in Figure 8.5. When the signal is applied to the inverting input (often given a negative sign), the output signal is of opposite phase (i.e. a negative input produces a' positive output). When applied to the non-inverting input (often given a positive sign), the phase of the output signal is not changed. For many applications, the input that is not used is connected to the 'earthy' or feedback part of the circuit.

Since an i.c. op-amp is a balanced differential amplifier, it requires a differential power supply; that is, a split supply with positive and negative outputs relative to the 'earthy' side of the circuit. Supply voltage is governed by the type of i.c., and the specification sheet gives absolute maximum ratings in addition to the normal working ratings.

Circuit (a) in Figure 8.5 represents an inverting amplifier, where the signal is applied through R_1 and the feedback

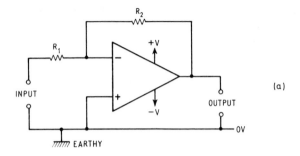

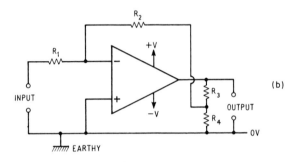

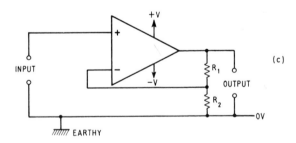

Figure 8.5. Basic i.c. op-amp feedback arrangements: (a) inverting amplifier with direct feedback, (b) inverting amplifier with tapped feedback, and (c) non-inverting amplifier

214

through R_2. In this case the gain (A) provided by the amplifier is virtually equal to R_2/R_1, on the assumption that R_1 and R_2 are much smaller than the input resistance of the i.c. and that A lies well within the intrinsic gain of the i.c. itself. This sort of circuit operates in the so-called *virtual earth* mode. This means that the inverting input is virtually at 'earth' potential and that the input resistance is defined essentially by R_1. This is because the d.c. feedback causes the stages in the i.c. to balance out so that the voltage between the two inputs goes very close to zero. For example, if the ratio R_2/R_1 is adjusted for a gain of, say, 20 dB (10 times) and the input signal is 0.2 V (200 mV), the output signal will obviously be 2 V. If the i.c. gain is 100 dB (100 000 times), then the signal at the inserting input will be $10/100\,000 \times 0.2$, or a mere 20 μV, which is pretty well close to nothing!

Arrangement (b) is adopted when the requirement is for high gain allied with relatively high input resistance. For this requirement, arrangement (a) would need a high R_2/R_1 ratio, which could make R_2 unrealistically high or R_1 lower than the input resistance requirement. By tapping the feedback with divider R_3/R_4 suitable values for R_1 and R_2 can be chosen more easily to satisfy the input resistance without the need to make R_2 unduly large. When R_2 is large compared with R_4 the gain is close to $R_2(R_3 + R_4)/R_1 \times R_4$.

A non-inverting feedback configuration is given at (c). Again the signal across the two inputs is close to zero, and when the input resistance of the i.c. is large compared with R_1 or R_2 the voltage across the latter resistor V_{R2} is very close to the input voltage V_{in}. The proportion of the output voltage V_{out} across R_2 is, of course, $V_{out} \times R_2/(R_1 + R_2)$ – normal potential-divider action – which means that V_{out} is equal to $V_{R2}(R_1 + R_2)/R_2$. Since the gain A is equal to V_{out}/V_{in}, we obtain $A = (R_1 + R_2)/R_2$.

One characteristic of the non-inverting amplifier (sometimes called a bootstrap circuit) is a very high input resistance, which can be hundreds of megohms, limited mainly by the impedance of the device at its input pins to 'earth'. However, there are practical difficulties that tend to restrict the use of the circuit from this point of view.

Although shown in Figure 8.5, the positive and negative supply inputs are not always included in i.c. circuit diagrams.

The degree of gain provided by an i.c. op-amp circuit is thus established by the value of the feedback resistors, the scheme being to start with an intrinsic gain far higher than the requirement and then to tailor the gain and the response characteristic to suit the application. Amplifiers are sometimes arranged for almost 100 per cent d.c. feedback so that amplification is given only to the a.c. signal, a technique that significantly reduces the d.c. offset at the output. A

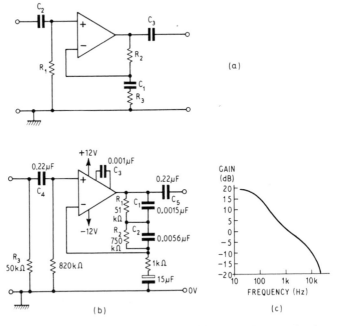

Figure 8.6. Circuit (a) provides a.c. amplification only since the d.c. feedback is virtually 100 per cent. This technique eliminates d.c. offset at the output. The reactive elements in the feedback circuit of (b) cause the gain to fall (feedback increasing) with increasing frequency; in this case, the components are chosen to provide RIAA equalisation for magnetic pickups (see Chapter 9), the response approximating that shown at (c)

216

non-inverting configuration of this type is given in Figure 8.6(a), where C_1 provides the a.c. feedback part of the signal as the result of its reactance. The midband gain of this circuit is equal to $(R_2 + R_3)/R_3$ and the input resistance is defined by R_1. Input and output couplings are commonly by capacitors. corresponding respectively to C_2 and C_3 in this circuit.

Reactive elements can also be used in the feedback circuit to provide almost any frequency/amplitude characteristic. The example given in Figure 8.6(b) provides RIAA equalisation (see page 223) for a magnetic gramophone pickup by giving the response approximated at (c). In this circuit the feedback increases with increasing frequency owing to the increasing reactance of C_1 and C_2, hence the reducing gain with increasing frequency, which provides the replay bass boost requirement to complement the RIAA recording characteristic. Time constants are formed by R_1/C_1 and by

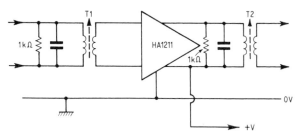

Figure 8.7. The use of an i.c. op-amp in the i.f. channel of an f.m. receiver

R_2/C_2 which, in conjunction with the other parameters of the circuit, give the turnover frequencies to suit the equalisation requirement. C_3 is a compensating capacitor, required by some i.c.s for stability of amplification over the frequency range of interest. The input resistance, and hence the load to the pickup cartridge, is defined essentially by R_3, while C_4 and C_5 are input and output coupling capacitors. To cater for the two stereo channels single encapsulations containing two i.c.s are available.

Tone-control circuits, filters, etc. can be tailored similarly by employing appropriate networks in the feedback circuit.

Integrated circuits are also found in i.f. amplifier stages of a.m. and f.m. radio receivers; one example of such an application is given in Figure 8.7, where T_1 and T_2 are the input and output i.f. bandpass coupling transformers and the 1 kΩ resistors are damping elements to provide the required passband.

Other applications include voltage regulation, audio pre- and power-amplification, stereo decoding, f.m. detection, etc. Indeed, some of the more recent devices developed for consumer electronics make it possible to develop complicated receivers (including colour television receivers) with the bare minimum of discrete components, as revealed from the sound-radio point of view in Chapter 10.

9

Microphone, pickup and loudspeaker

The microphone and gramophone pickup generate *programme signals* and the loudspeaker changes them back to sound so that they can be heard. Most programme material starts as sound waves, so the first link in the broadcasting chain is generally the microphone. This changes the sound waves to weak electrical signals, which are the programme signals. After suitable amplification and processing, the signals are fed either to the transmitter for direct broadcasting or to a magnetic tape recorder for storing and subsequent broadcasting or for gramophone (disc) record making. The programme information stored in the groove spiral of a gramophone record in the form of 'wriggles' is changed back to programme signal whenever required by the gramophone pickup, which consists of a pickup cartridge and arm combination. The cartridge, which is equipped with a stylus for tracing the groove spiral, is fitted to the end of the arm (usually in a headshell), while the other end of the arm is commonly pivoted in such a way as to allow the cartridge to traverse the record with the very minimum of friction.

The microphone, gramophone pickup and loudspeaker are called *transducers* because they change sound to signal or signal to sound. Several principles can be used for the transducing effect, the three most common ones being electromagnetic, piezoelectric and electrostatic.

Electromagnetic principle

The vast majority of modern gramophone pickup utilise the electromagnetic principle, whereby vibrations, imparted to the stylus as a result of its tracing the groove-wall modulation ('wriggles'), result in magnetic-flux changes relative to a coil of wire. A signal e.m.f. is thus induced into the winding and a signal voltage, corresponding to the original signal information is developed across it. This, of course, is the dynamo effect, which was discussed in Chapter 1.

The groove of a gramophone record is of a V-shaped cut, and for stereo one wall is modulated with the left signal and the other with the right signal. Thus a stereo pickup has two such generating systems, one yielding the left signal and the other the right signal, the design being such that minimal interaction, and hence crosstalk, occurs between the two channels. Readers requiring more information on this technique, called the 45/45 technique of stereo recording, may find the author's *The Audio Handbook* of interest, also published by Newnes Technical Books.

Many microphones also adopt the electromagnetic principle. In this case a low-mass diaphragm is coupled to the eletromagnetic system, and as the diaphragm vibrates in the presence of sound waves, so a corresponding signal voltage is developed across the winding. Some stereo microphones employ two such 'generators' in a common housing, so that the axis of one is at right angles to that of the other.

The electromagnetic principle of microphones is exemplified by the moving-coil arrangement, where a coil of wire free to move in a strong magnetic field is secured to the centre of the diaphragm. As the diaphragm vibrates so the turns of the coil cut the magnetic lines of force and a signal voltage corresponding to the information carried by the sound waves is developed across the winding.

Many loudspeakers use the moving-coil principle, but in the reciprocal sense; that is, signal current (after the programme signal has been significantly boosted by power amplification) is caused to flow through the coil. The resulting magnetic field, which is changing in accordance with the programme signal, reacts against the fixed magnetic field in which the coil is suspended. The coil thus vibrates (the motor effect, Chapter 1) within the fixed field and carries the diaphragm or cone with it, thereby producing sound waves.

The vital parts of a moving-coil loudspeaker are illustrated in Figure 9.1.

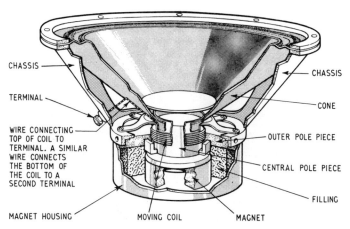

Figure 9.1. The vital elements of a moving-coil loudspeaker unit

For high-quality sound reproduction a loudspeaker system often has two or more moving-coil units in its enclosure, each handling a certain part of the sound spectrum.

The ranges of frequencies are channelled separately to the units by way of frequency-divider filters – sometimes called *crossover filters*. A high-pass section feeds the high frequencies to the tweeter, a bandpass section the middle frequencies to the squawker and a low-pass section the low frequencies to the woofer. In this way each unit receives only the range of frequencies it is best able to reproduce.

The woofer in particular needs to be mounted on some sort of baffle board to isolate accoustically the front of the cone from the back. Without such isolation sound waves from the back of the cone tend to interfere with and cancel those from the front of the cone, particularly as the sound wavelength increases with decreasing frequency. Without suitable baffling a woofer cannot reproduce the bass register.

The loudspeaker unit used in the simple radio receiver is called upon to handle the entire frequency spectrum, and for baffling reliance is placed on the front panel of the cabinet to isolate the sound waves between the front and the back of the cone. Thus the quality of reproduction from such a receiver can never be very high.

Some pickup cartridges also are based on the moving-coil principle, and a very interesting photograph of the moving-coil element, coupled to the end to the stylus cantilever, of

Figure 9.2. Moving-coil assembly coupled to the stylus cantilever of the On Life moving-coil pickup cartridge. In reality this is of microscopic proportions

such a cartridge is given in Figure 9.2. Although looking rather like the coils of a larger dynamo, the assembly in reality is of microscopic proportions. There are separate coils for the left and right channels.

Equalisation

When gramophone records are made the higher recording frequencies are boosted and the lower ones attenuated relative to the middle frequencies. The former improves the replay signal-to-noise ratio because the replay equalisation restores the high-frequency balanced by attenuation, which at the same time reduces the noise. The latter ensures that the amplitude of vibration of the recording stylus is retained at a value that avoids the need for excessively wide groove spacing when low-frequency, large-amplitude signals are being recorded, the low-frequency balance being restored on replay by corresponding amplification. The characteristic defining the type and amount of recording treble boost and bass cut, and replay treble cut and bass boost, in current use is that originally evolved by the Record Industry Association of America (there is also an equivalent British standard), and is thus called the *RIAA characteristic* or *standard*.

The net result is that the modulation has an essentially constant amplitude characteristic, which means that the velocity increases with frequency at the rate of 6 dB/octave. Now, since the electrical output delivered by an electromagnetic cartridge depends on the rate of cutting of the magnetic flux (i.e. on the velocity), a record recorded to the RIAA standard with a tone starting at a low frequency and progressively increasing to a high frequency ('swept tone') will give an output rising with frequency when replayed with such a cartridge.

A 'flat' response is achieved by *equalisation*; that is, by passing the cartridge signal through an amplifier having a frequency/amplitude characteristic like that shown in Figure 8.6(c). All electromagnetic cartridges require this sort of equalisation, and since the cartridge output is also relatively

223

small (about 5 mV nominal – and less than this from a moving-coil species) a fair degree of preamplification is also required.

Piezoelectric principle

When certain crystalline materials are stressed, an electric charge is developed across their surfaces. This is called piezoelectricity. Certain natural water-soluble crystals exhibit the effect, and are used in so-called crystal microphones, pickups and, sometimes, loudspeaker units. Of recent years a ceramic material, processed under the influence of a strong electrostatic field, has been developed as a more robust man-made substitute for the natural crystals, and it is from this material that ceramic piezoelectric transducers are made. While the stressing produces electricity, the application of electricity yields stressing or flexing of the ceramic, hence the material's suitability for both 'generator' and 'motor' applications.

Because the electric output is proportional to the amplitude of the stressing or flexing, the output of a ceramic pickup is proportional to the amplitude of the groove 'wriggles' or modulation, which means that the output from such a pickup playing a record made to the RIAA standard is essentially 'flat' over the frequency spectrum. The equalisation required for an electromagnetic pickup is thus not needed when a ceramic pickup is loaded into a high-value resistance. The small amount of equalisation necessary accurately to tailor the frequency/amplitude response is sometimes attended to by mechanical means inside the cartridge.

The piezoelectric source is capacitive, so to avoid bass attenuation it needs to be loaded (from the input circuit of the amplifier) by a high-value resistance, which is of several megohms, as distinct from the 47 kilohms loading requirement of many electromagnetic pickups. When a lower-valve load is used the output tends towards the velocity output of the electromagnetic pickup, and this artifice is sometimes adopted so that a ceramic pickup can be connected into the magnetic (equalised) input of an amplifier. The output of a ceramic cartridge is generally several times that of an electromagnetic cartridge, so signal attenuation may have to be applied to avoid overloading the low-level magnetic input of an amplifier; but the low-value loading goes some way towards satisfying this requirement.

Electrostatic principle

One manifestation of the electrostatic principle is the capacitor microphone. Here a very thin diaphragm serves as one plate of a capacitor, the other plate being fixed. As the diaphragm vibrates in the presence of sound waves so the capacitance varies in accordance with the information carried by the waves. The capacitor is 'polarised' by a direct voltage applied through a high value of resistance. Since the quantity of the charge (q) in coulombs acquired by a capacitance (C) is related to the voltage (V) in accordance with $q = CV$, it follows that a change in C will yield a proportional change in q. Thus, as C varies in sympathy with the sound waves so current flows into and out of C through the series resistance, with the result that signal voltage is developed across the resistance.

One coulomb of charge is equal to 1 ampere flowing for 1 second, and a capacitance of 1 farad will take a charge of 1 coulomb when the potential across it is 1 volt. Since the change in capacitance is very small, a mere few picofarads ($1 \text{pF} = 10^{-12} \text{F}$), the current flowing through the resistance and hence the voltage developed across it will also be very small. The resulting programme signal thus needs to be amplified significantly, and this is accomplished by a head amplifier incorporating a field effect transistor, which keeps the input impedance high (i.e. it avoids the very small source signal from being unduly attenuated by parallel resistance and capacitance).

The electrostatic principle is also used in some loudspeaker systems. In this case the diaphragm has a much larger area

225

than in the microphone, and the total area may be extended by the use of several sections. When charges are applied across the capacitance from suitably amplified signal voltage, the diaphragm plate is attracted to or repelled from the fixed plate, and in this way sound waves are produced, as with cone loudspeakers.

A high polarising voltage is used to minimise frequency-doubling and hence second-harmonic distortion, and as a further aid towards improved linearity the diaphragm plate may be equally spaced between two fixed and perforated plates. When this is done a sort of 'push-pull' driving system is adopted, whereby the diaphragm plate is energised relative to the two fixed plates by a transformer with a centre-tapped secondary winding. Thus during one half-cycle of signal the diaphragm plate is attracted to one of the fixed plates and repelled by the other, while during the other half-cycle the attracting and repelling actions are reversed.

The latest headphone sets (one ear unit for the left channel and the other for the right channel of a stereo signal) are also based on the moving-coil loudspeaker principle; in fact, in many ear units the elements look like miniature loudspeaker units. The bass response is maintained, in spite of the small cones or diaphragms, owing to the close acoustical coupling of the units to the ears.

More expensive headphone sets incorporate the electrostatic principle, being operated via a separate driving unit (which also provides the polarising voltage) from the radio receiver or amplifier.

Less expensive headphone sets, and some of the small earpieces used for personal listening to small transistor radios, are based on the piezoelectric principle.

A recent development of the electrostatic principle eliminates the need for a polarising voltage, which is effectively 'built in' during the processing. This, called 'electret', is also found in some recent pickup cartridges – the Japanese Toshiba S401S, for example.

10

Radio receivers

A radio receiver is an assembly of solid-state devices (Chapter 7), possibly integrated circuits (Chapter 8) and discrete components (Chapter 6), and the principles involved are precisely in accordance with those expounded in Chapter 5. The mono receiver is equipped with a solitary audio channel and loudspeaker system (Chapter 9), while a stereo receiver includes a stereo decoder (Chapter 5) and two audio channels and loudspeaker systems, and is designed to operate in Band 2 (the f.m. band, Chapter 2) as well as, possibly, in the a.m. bands.

The receiver may be battery- or mains-powered, and some models are equipped with facilities for both modes of powering. The small transistor portable is invariably battery-powered, and the a.m. signals are picked up by an inbuilt ferrite-rod aerial (Chapter 3). When such a receiver also incorporates facilities for f.m. reception, the signals in Band 2 are picked up either by an inbuilt telescopic rod aerial or by an external f.m. aerial coupled to the receiver through feeder cable (Chapter 3).

Some receivers, even portable designs, include a cassette tape machine allowing the recording of radio programmes from its own receiver, as well as the replay of previously recorded cassettes and 'factory'-made music cassettes. Another integration is the radio receiver/record deck, yielding the latter-day version of the earlier radiogram. More eleborate models may integrate both a cassette machine and record deck ('Music Centre').

From the basic mono-only receiver we pass through the intermediate area of the quasi- or 'budget' hi-fi systems which, although in advance of the potential of reproduction afforded by the small transistor radio and capable of stereo reproduction with two external loudspeaker systems, are not regarded as 'real hi-fi' by the staunch enthusiast or hi-fi devotee (audiophile).

Transistor receiver

Although taken from an earlier edition of this book, the circuit in Figure 10.1 is still representative of the portable class of transistor receiver. Starting at the left-hand side of the circuit we have the ferrite-rod aerial which is equipped with windings for the long and medium wavebands (L_2 and L_3 respectively). The aerial winding selected by switch section S_2 is tuned by VC_1, and m.w. trimming is by TC_2 and l.w. trimming by TC_1, which is shorted out with S_1 in the m.w. position, as shown (Chapter 5). Transistor Tr_1 operates as a

Figure 10.1. Circuit diagram of transistor portable radio (see text)

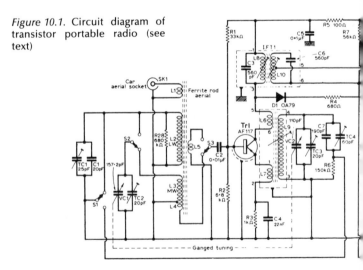

self-oscillating mixer (frequency changer) and S_3 selects the aerial winding coupled to its base via C_2 (coupling capacitor). The l.w. winding is coupled by L_5 and the m.w. winding by L_4, the latter with L_3 forming an auto-transformer (Chapter 6). Such coupling coils are required to achieve the correct impedance match to Tr_1 base (Chapter 6). The additional winding L_1 is included on the ferrite-rod aerial so that the signal from an external aerial can be coupled in, such as a telescopic aerial when the receiver is being used in a car and the ferrite-rod aerial is screened by the metal body.

Tr_1 is also arranged as the local oscillator (Chapter 5), the coupling for *positive feedback* being from collector winding L_6 to emitter winding L_7. Winding L_9 tunes the oscillator in conjunction with VC_2. It will be appreciated from Chapter 5, of course, that VC_1 and VC_2 are mechanically ganged and that the displacement between the incoming signal frequency and the oscillator frequency is maintained at the intermediate-frequency difference over the l.w. and m.w. bands. It should also be noted that switch sections $S_1/S_2/S_3$ are ganged. M.W. oscillator trimming is by TC_3 and l.w. trimming by TC_4,

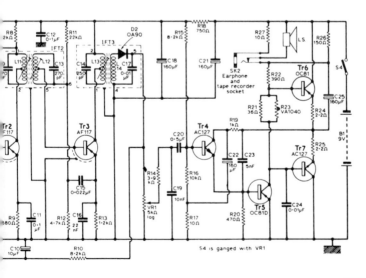

the latter being brought into circuit by S_1 in the l.w. position (the other position to that shown). In the m.w. position R_6 and the relatively low series impedance of TC_4 and C_7 in parallel (Chapter 6) damp the oscillator circuit and hence reduce the signal amplitude.

Tr_1 base is biased by R_1/R_2, while the emitter resistor R_3 with C_4 in parallel serves to set the oscillator signal amplitude as well as providing thermal runaway protection (Chapter 7).

I.F. stages

The i.f. signal is developed across the primary L_8 of the first i.f. transformer. IFT_1. The signal is coupled to the secondary L_{10} and a tap on this winding couples the i.f. signal at the correct impedance to the base of Tr_2, which is the first i.f. amplifier transistor, whose base is biased by R_7 and by an a.g.c. (automatic gain control) potential – see later. Diode D_1 maintains a predetermined signal amplitude in the event of a very strong transmission by conducting and shunting L_8 by R_8, thereby reducing its Q factor.

The amplified i.f. signal at Tr_2 collector is tuned by L_{11} of IFT_2 and coupled to another i.f. stage, Tr_3, by L_{12}, the tappings on these windings providing the correct impedance matchings. The third i.f. transformer is IFT_3 and the secondary (L_{14}) of this feeds the a.m. detector diode D_2, so that audio signal is developed across the load VR_1, which is the volume control (Chapter 5). Note that the windings of the i.f. transformers are fixed tuned by capacitors and pretuned by ferrite cores. These are merely presets, of course, which are adjusted to optimise the i.f. channel performance.

A.G.C.

The d.c. component of the demodulated i.f. signal appearing across VR_1 is applied to Tr_2 base via R_{10}/L_{10} and thus appears with the standing bias obtained from R_7. Now, the d.c. from the detector diode is positive since it emanates from the

230

cathode, and its value depends on the amplitude of the incoming signal. Thus if the amplitude of the incoming signal increases so also will the positive potential at Tr_2 base. Since the transistor is a pnp type the collector/emitter current and stage gain fall, thereby providing automatic gain control. The audio component is filtered by R_{10} and C_{10}.

A.F. section

The audio component remains across VR_1 because of the 'hold-off' effect of R_{10}. The required level of signal is tapped off by the slider of the volume control (Chapter 6) and fed through R_{14}/C_{20} to the base of the first audio amplifier stage Tr_4. C_{20} removes the d.c. component of the demodulated signal while R_{14}/C_{19} filter out the i.c. component. Tr_4 thus receives only audio signal.

Tr_4 emitter is in direct communication with driver transistor Tr_5 base, while Tr_5 collector is in direct communication with the bases of the pnp/npn (complementary pair) output transistors. Tr_6/Tr_7. The emitters of the output transistors then couple to the loudspeaker (LS) through coupling electrolytic C_{25}.

Excluding the loudspeaker, therefore, the whole of the audio section is directly coupled. Now, because the output transistors constitute a complementary pair, a positive-going drive signal from Tr_5 will push one into conduction and pull the other away from conduction (into non-conduction), thereby yielding a push-pull action. The conduction conditions reverse, of course, on the opposite half-cycle of drive signal.

The stage is biased so that in the absence of drive signal only a small current (called quiescent current) is taken by the output transistors. In other words, these transistors are biased towards class B. The small quiescent current is necessary to avoid discontinuity of the overall transfer characteristic when one transistor switches off and the other switches on. Bad discontinuity would occur without quiescent current and a rather nasty brand of distortion, called

231

crossover distortion, would mar the reproduction, particularly at low signal levels.

The current, of course, rises with increasing level of drive signal, so that the power consumed by the receiver is dependent on the level of operation. The thermistor R_{23} holds the quiescent current fairly constant with increasing temperature of the transistors.

The circuit also has facilities for the connection of an earphone or for the extraction of signal for tape recording. The jack socket SK_2 is switched so that when a jack plug is inserted the loudspeaker is disconnected and the output signal made available for the other purposes.

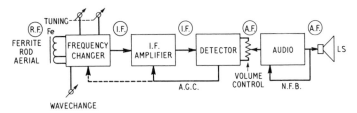

Figure 10.2. Block diagram summarising the circuit given in Figure 10.1

The block diagram in Figure 10.2 summarises the type of radio receiver described, while also showing the application of negative feedback in the audio section – from the output back to some point at the input of the same section.

Negative feedback

Negative feedback with respect to integrated-circuit operational amplifiers was investigated in Chapter 8. It is also used extensively in the audio stages of radio receivers and in hi-fi amplifiers. As when used with i.c. op-amps, it reduces the distortion and increases the upper-frequency response over a flat frequency/amplitude characteristic, but at the expense of gain. The way that it improves the frequency response was shown in Figure 8.4.

With *negative* feedback a sample of the signal at the output of an amplifier is fed back to the input, but at 180 degrees out of phase with the input signal. The two signals are then added together. Owing to the antiphase condition, the net signal active at the input is diminished by the amount of the feedback, which means that the distortion at the output is reduced by the same amount.

Positive feedback

Positive feedback works the other way round. That is, the signal fed back is in phase with the input, with the result that the stage gain is enhanced. Beyond a certain critical point, the amplifier changes into an oscillator and generates a sustained signal related to the resonance of circuit elements. The local oscillator in Figure 10.1 works like this, the resonance and hence frequency being determined in this case by the oscillator tuned circuit.

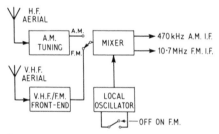

Figure 10.3. Block diagram of first stages of f.m./a.m. receiver

D.C. negative feedback in the audio section is taken from R_{24}/R_{25} junction back to Tr_4 collector via R_{19}, which also provides d.c. stabilisation. Feedback is also applied to Tr_4 base via C_{22}. High-frequency feedback is reduced by C_{23}/R_{20}, and this is often done to prevent the feedback changing to positive at high frequencies as the result of phase shift through the circuits.

Relatively inexpensive f.m./a.m. receivers employ a composite i.f. channel containing i.f. tuned circuits for both f.m.

(10.7 MHz) and a.m. (470 kHz). The required detector is switched in by the mode control, which also brings in a separate front end for f.m. while muting the a.m. local oscillator, as shown by the block diagram in Figure 10.3. The circuit of an f.m. front end, using field effect transistors, was given in Figure 7.27.

More expensive f.m./a.m. receivers use separate f.m. and a.m. i.f. channels with their own front ends and detectors. This type of receiver is more in the accepted hi-fi category. F.M. detector circuits were given in Figure 5.20.

More receivers, even relatively inexpensive models, are adopting the ceramic-filter type of bandpass coupling for the i.f. channel (see Figure 5.19) and varicap tuning (see Figure 7.18) for the f.m. front-end.

Use of i.c.s

Integrated circuits are also in common use particularly in the i.f. channels and for stereo decoding, f.m. detection (quadrature detector) and preamplification. Indeed, Mullard have produced an i.c. (TBA570) which, excluding the front ends, provides all the active requirements for the small-signal receiving sections (not power amplification). It includes a signal detector, i.f. amplifier, mixer, local oscillator and a.g.c. for a.m.; a.m. limiter, complete i.f. channel and front-end bias stabilisation for f.m.; and a driver and preamplifier for audio. The design is for use with ceramic filters, and the audio output is sufficient for driving a pair of complementary push-pull output transistors (as in Figure 10.1) for 3 W output using AC187/188s or for 5 W using AD161/162s. The circuit of the i.c. is given in Figure 10.4. This, in conjunction with discrete components and a power-amplifier stage, will thus make up a complete receiver!

There are hosts of other composite i.c.s, many developed by Mullard, including the TDA1200, which can form the basis of an f.m. receiver since it includes the stages shown in Figure 10.5. For stereo decoding there is the latest RCA

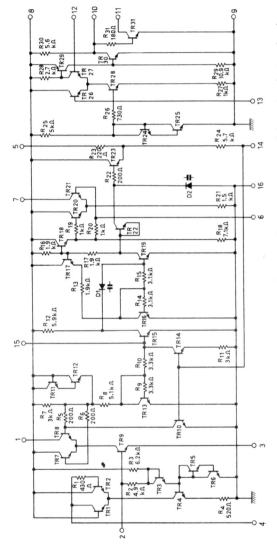

Figure 10.4. Circuit of the Mullard TBA570 integrated circuit. This contains most of the active devices for the small-signal stages of a complete f.m./a.m. receiver

235

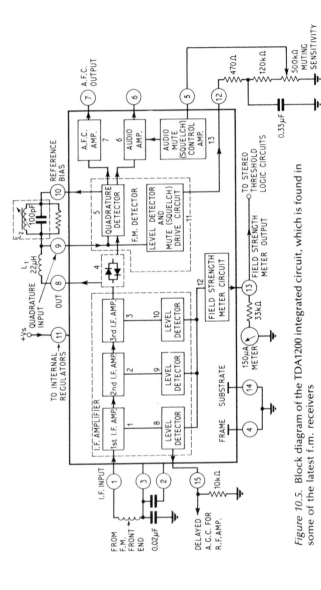

Figure 10.5. Block diagram of the TDA1200 integrated circuit, which is found in some of the latest f.m. receivers

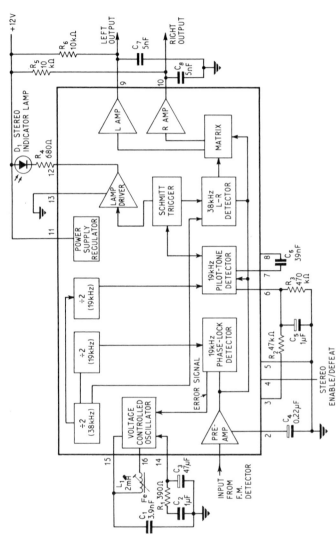

Figure 10.6. Block diagram of the various stages in the RCA CA3090AQ stereo decoder integrated circuit

237

CA3090AQ, whose block diagram is given in Figure 10.6 (see also the last part of Chapter 5).

The modern radio receiver, although inherently complex, thus appears to be less complicated because many of the components that at one time were discrete are now contained within a small encapsulation and based on the monolithic silicon integrated circuit or thick- or thin-film integrated microcircuit. Also, of course, point-to-point wiring has long been superseded by the printed circuit board, the more complicated type of receiver using several of these in 'module' form.

More receivers are now using frequency synthesisation for generating the local oscillator signal which, with a quartz crystal reference oscillator and phase-lock loop, are capable of very accurate tuning with hardly any frequency drift. Rather than the old-style scale and cursor, the tuned frequency is commonly indicated digitally. Tuning is handled by the varicap instead of mechanical capacitor gangs, and some of the recent domestic receivers and tuners are equipped with press-button station selection, some even with digital-type circuits (based on i.c.s.) allowing scanning of the stored tuning data.

Communications transceivers also now commonly adopt frequency synthesisation (see Chapter 4) for both the receive and transmit sections. An illustration of this technique is given in the following chapter dealing with CB transceivers.

Hi-fi equipment

Hi-fi stands for high-fidelity – sound reproduction as close as possible to the original. Hi-fi equipment designed for receiving and amplifying the programme signals is of a particularly high order – generally above that of ordinary domestic radio equipment.

Readers wishing to delve into this exciting subject may find the author's *The Audio Handbook* of interest (also published by Newnes Technical Books).

11

Citizen's Band radio

Since the previous edition of this book we have seen the introduction of citizen's band radio (CB) in the UK – formerly called the 'open channel'. It is appropriate, therefore, that a chapter on the subject should be presented in this new edition. Authority has been given by the Government to

Table 11.1. Frequencies corresponding to the 40 channels of 27 MHz CB, where it will be seen that the spacing between each one is 10 kHz

Channel	Frequency (MH$_z$)	Channel	Frequency (MH$_z$)
1	27.60125	21	27.80125
2	27.61125	22	27.81125
3	27.62125	23	27.82125
4	27.63125	24	27.83125
5	27.64125	25	27.84125
6	27.65125	26	27.85125
7	27.66125	27	27.86125
8	27.67125	28	27.87125
9	27.68125	29	27.88125
10	27.69125	30	27.89125
11	27.70125	31	27.90125
12	27.71125	32	27.91125
13	27.72125	33	27.92125
14	27.73125	34	27.93125
15	27.74125	35	27.94125
16	27.75125	36	27.95125
17	27.76125	37	27.96125
18	27.77125	38	27.97125
19	27.78125	39	27.98125
20	27.79125	40	27.99125

allow the licencing of transceivers (transmitter combined with receiver) within two frequency bands. One band lies at the top of h.f., just below the 28 MHz amateur radio band and is divided into 40 channels with 10 kHz separation between them as shown in Table 11.1. The other is in the ultra-high-frequency (u.h.f.) region and is at present divided into 20 channels with 50 kHz spacing between them as shown in Table 11.2(a).

Table 11.2(a). Frequencies corresponding to the 20 channels of 934 MHz CB, where it will be seen that the spacing between each one is 50 kHz. This provides room for a possible additional 20 channels, making 40 in total, by reducing the spacing to 25 kHz

Channel	Frequency (MHz)	Channel	Frequency (MHz)
1	934.025	11	934.525
2	934.075	12	934.575
3	934.125	13	934.625
4	934.175	14	934.675
5	934.225	15	934.725
6	934.275	16	934.775
7	934.325	17	934.825
8	934.375	18	934.875
9	934.425	19	934.925
10	934.475	20	934.975

Table 11.2(b). 934 MHz CB frequencies based on the CEPT band plan enabling the future use of 25 kHz channelling. All these frequencies are shifted down by 12.5 kHz from those shown in Table 11.2(a)

Channel	Frequency (MHz)	Channel	Frequency (MHz)
1	934.0125	11	934.5125
2	934.0625	12	934.5625
3	934.1125	13	934.6125
4	934.1625	14	934.6625
5	934.2125	15	934.7125
6	934.2625	16	934.7625
7	934.3125	17	934.8125
8	934.3625	18	934.8625
9	934.4125	19	934.9125
10	934.4625	20	934.9625

240

However, it is the Home Office's aim to realign the u.h.f. channels by moving each one 12.5 kHz downwards as shown in Table 11.2(b) to conform to the 943 MHz CB channel plan produced by the European Post and Telecommunications Administrations (CEPT), which is based on 25 kHz channelling. It is proposed that the sale, by manufacturer or importation, of equipment using the Table 11.2(a) channels should not continue beyond 30 April 1984 and that their use should not be permitted after 31 December 1987.

Licence conditions differ significantly from those of amateur radio, which are much more stringent, and it is not required to pass an examination to obtain a licence. Virtually anyone can obtain a licence on payment of the requisite fee. A single licence covers the employment of up to three transceivers and the basic conditions of use are minimal (some regard this as a great pity). Only plain speech transmissions are permitted, based on f.m. with 2.5 kHz maximum deviation on the 27 MHz band and angle-modulation with 5 kHz maximum deviation on the 934 MHz band. Angle- or phase-modulation is a form of f.m. with a change of modulation characteristics more suited to u.h.f., where the phase angle of the carrier wave is the parameter varied.

Radio frequency (r.f.) output of the transmitter must not exceed 4 W on the 27 MHz band and 8 W on the 934 MHz band (except with hand-held sets where the effective radiated power is limited to a maximum of 3 W). On the 27 MHz band, however, the effective radiated power (e.r.p.) cannot be enhanced by the use of a directional aerial or co-linear type. In fact, the conditions make it illegal even to use a fully-dimensioned half-wave dipole. The 27 MHz aerial must not exceed 1.5 m in length, and to render it resonant in relation to a ground plane or counterpoise of some form it needs to be loaded at the bottom by an inductor, which is another requirement (see Chapter 3).

In other words, the aerial is generally a shortened quarter-wave rod with bottom inductive loading to which the inner conductor of the coaxial feeder (50 ohms) is connected. The braid of the coax then connects to the ground plane either directly or capacitively, the latter commonly when the metal body of a motor car (mobile working) forms the ground plane. For home-base operation the ground plane is often formed by a single rod or multiplicity of rods, depending on the nature of the aerial (see Chapter 3). Vertical polarisation of the radio wave is adopted (e.g. the aerial is vertically disposed).

The conditions are eased on the 934 MHz band since a directional aerial can here be used quite legally up to a maximum of four elements (e.g. Yagi aerial), which could yield some 4 to 5 dB power gain in the forward direction. However, each element is limited to a 17 cm length restriction. Even so, assuming a net gain of 3 dB (after taking account of the forward gain and signal loss in the coaxial feeder), this still allows a healthy 16 W e.r.p. in the forward direction, which more or less puts the range potential on par with that at 27 MHz – from the signal point of view.

However, the greater peak deviation allowed at 934 MHz improves the signal/noise ratio quite significantly and this in itself makes it easier to read weak signals. Speech quality would also seem to be better at u.h.f. owing to the less restricted audio passband.

The e.r.p. at 27 MHz is less than the 4 W of transmitter r.f. permitted owing to the restrictions on the aerial. Nevertheless, with a well-designed 27 MHz legal CB aerial an e.r.p. up to around 2 W (omnidirectional) is not impossible. The reduction in e.r.p. stems from the smaller radiation resistance of the shortened quarter-wave aerial and the losses in the loading inductor and ground plane.

Most CB interest has developed around the 27 MHz band owing mainly to the dearth of 934 MHz equipment, the greater cost of this equipment, including the need for more expensive low-loss coaxial cable and SWR meters and ancillary items which work correctly at approaching 1 GHz.

It is sad to relate that in some quarters CB has been brought into disrepute owing to laxity in operating procedures which often appear to be deliberately directed at the more serious CBer; the use of maladjusted power microphones which increase the peak deviation and hence the modulation index, resulting in excessive 'breakthrough' of the signal into an adjacent channel; and the use of 27 MHz aerials which produce a greater e.r.p. than the system as a whole can accommodate, thereby causing 'blocking' of receivers in proximity, even when receiving on an entirely different channel. Another factor is that aerials are not uncommonly mounted at more than 7 m above ground at 27 MHz. While this in itself is not wrong, it is nevertheless illegal to transmit on 27 MHz at the full 4 W r.f. when the aerial is higher than 7 m. The Home Office requirement here is for 10 dB attenuation (power reduction of 10 times) when the height of the aerial exceeds 7 m (10 m at 934 MHz).

Happily the use of powerful (expressly illegal) linear amplifiers is on the wane. These really can play havoc to the CB system in a local area by completely blocking relatively weak signals from almost all channels, while having the potential to cause serious interference to protected services like the police, fire, etc. under certain conditions.

Here are some of the salient points from the licencing conditions.

(a) Equipment must be designed, constructed and maintained to avoid undue interference to wireless telegraphy.
(b) All transmissions, except for selective calling signals, to be in plain speech only (thus prohibiting the transmission of music!).
(c) Use in aircraft or airborne vehicle not allowed.
(d) Transmissions of a grossly offensive, indecent or obscene character prohibited.
(e) Use for advertising or soliciting goods or services prohibited.
(f) 27 MHz antenna shall not be more than 1.5 m in length, and must be base-loaded. 934 MHz antenna shall consist of a maximum of four elements, none of which may exceed 17 cm in length.

There are penalties under Section 1 of the Wireless Telegraphy Act 1949 (currently being updated) which can be incurred should the licencing conditions be infringed.

CB DX

As mentioned earlier, the system was first introduced as an 'open channel', permitting general chit-chat – often protracted! However, some of the more technically-minded saw it as an extension to their interest in radio and started to use it as a sort of quasi-amateur radio band. This was encouraged by the unwise choice of 27 MHz which, during certain times, is subject to sky-wave propagation and hence is supportive of long-distance communication. Thus, CB DX calls (typical of those heard on the amateur radio bands) are often heard on CB during enhanced propagation conditions. It is normally the space-wave which supports 27 MHz CB; but during late spring and summer the onset of sporadic E (E_s) significantly increases the communication path. Contacts on 27 MHz CB have been made from the bottom of the country right up to the top of Scotland and into the Orkney and Shetland Islands, and also well into Europe – on f.m.! While such contacts are singularly unreliable, they are of immense interest to the enthusiast. Less fleeting contacts are possible at that frequency over far greater distances during a high sunspot count.

Tropospheric propagation, sometimes mixed with E_s, has also been detected on 27 MHz; but this mode of propagation has a greater prevalence at higher frequencies, so during a so-called 'tropo lift' 934 MHz transmissions can well exceed the normal space-wave radio horizon distance. E_s propagation is rarely if ever experienced at 934 MHz, neither normal ionospheric circuits. This is because at these ultra-high frequencies the radio wave passes through the ionised layers and vanishes into space (see Chapter 3).

CB DXing and local chit-chat are incompatible, and the resulting 'CB friction' has encouraged the more technically enthusiastic CBer to consider the amateur radio bands for satisfaction. This has resulted in a remarkable increase in the number of CBers studying for, and successfully sitting, the Radio Amateur Examination (RAE). The open-channel chit-chat CBer, however, is still often bugged by interference from distant stations during the times when the 27 MHz band

244

exhibits enhanced propagation. This is sometimes so severe as to make it almost impossible to communicate locally except with close and hence very strong stations.

934 MHz CB is plagued less in this respect which, coupled with the improved signal/noise ratio and (at the time of writing) less busy channels, would seem to be encouraging the more professional class of CBer to adopt the u.h.f. channels. Alternatively, this class of user could make use of *selective calling* which is a feature enabling a call to be made and detected without the need for continuous monitoring (see page 255).

CB transceiver principles

Bearing in mind the relatively low price of CB sets, their electronics are outstandingly sophisticated and state-of-art and, owing to the stringent technical requirements placed on them by the Home Office, they are remarkably stable and in the main accurate. To avoid incorrect frequency operation and to ensure precise channel accuracy the transceivers employ frequency synthesisation (see page 82), the accuracy of which (on all channels) is governed by a quartz oscillator. Synthesisation is controlled in terms of CB channel number by a digital code which is monitored by a read-only memory (ROM), this being part of the phase-lock loop integrated circuit (i.c.). Access occurs only when the applied input code corresponds to the code implanted in the ROM, the output then being on one of the legal CB channels. The input coding is established by the channel selector switch. The ROM makes it virtually impossible to attain a transmission frequency which has not been legally assigned for CB.

This part of the circuit (in block-diagram form) appropriate to the excellent *Cybernet Beta 3000* is given in Figure 11.1. Here the voltage-controlled oscillator (v.c.o.) is arranged to oscillate around 13 MHz during transmit and 17 MHz during receive. The frequency is reduced in transmit by transistor Q2 applying additional oscillator capacitance (including trimmer CT1) when the transmitter is activated. A varicap

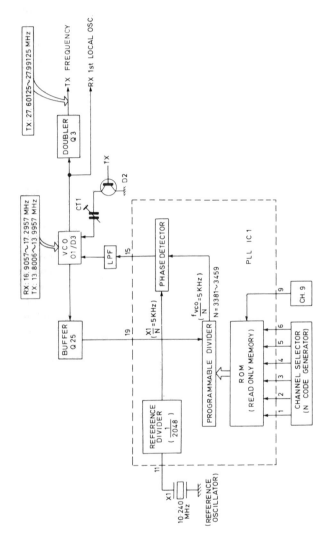

Figure 11.1. Frequency-synthesising and phase-lock loop part of the Beta 3000 CB transceiver

diode is also connected in the oscillator circuit such that a change in d.c. voltage at its cathode also changes the frequency of the v.c.o.

The channel selector produces 6-digit BCD codes, a code for each of the 40 channels, and the channel number selected by rotation of the switch is shown by a l.e.d. display on the front panel. The codes involved are given in the frequency chart, Table 11.3 where, for example, it can be seen that the code is 100100 in the channel 9 position. Only when one of these codes for the legal CB channels has been obtained will the oscillator function. This is because the code is compared with that implanted in the ROM for the legal channels.

The programmable-divider part of the i.c. is set by the ROM, the divide-down being that of the v.c.o. after passing through the buffer amplifier Q25. The dividing ratio is thus 'monitored' by the ROM and established by the setting of the channel selector switch. The divided v.c.o. frequency is fed to the phase detector part of the i.c. along with a divided signal from the 10.240 MHz reference crystal oscillator X1 (trimmed for precise channel accuracy by a trimmer capacitor). The reference divider handles this latter operation in the ratio of 1/2048, thereby yielding a fixed output frequency close to 5 kHz.

The phase detector compares the two input signals in terms of frequency and hence phase. Any lack of correlation produces a d.c. output. After smoothing and filtering by the low-pass filter (l.p.f.) this is applied to the cathode of the varicap diode in the v.c.o. circuit such that the v.c.o. output is corrected to be precisely coincident with that from the reference divider. The loop is then in the locked condition and the v.c.o. output is held to tight frequency tolerance by the quartz reference.

The v.c.o. output frequency, of course, depends on the ratio (N) of the programmable divider which is set by the channel selector switch. N goes from 3381 (channel 1) to 3459 (channel 40) as shown in Table 11.3, receive mode. Let us suppose that channel 36 is selected corresponding to a program code of 011011 and a receive divisor of 3451. The v.c.o. output frequency would then be close to 0.005 Mz (the

Table 11.3. Program codes, channel and V.C.O. frequencies and receive and transmit divisor ratios appertaining to the Cybernet Beta 3000 transceivers and other Beta transceivers

Channel	Channel frequency (MHz)	Program code						RX (T/R = 1) Divisor	V.C.O. frequency	TX (T/R = 0) Divisor	V.C.O. frequency
		D_1	D_2	D_3	D_4	D_5	D_6				
1	27.60125	1	0	0	0	0	0	3381	16.9057	2760	13.8006
2	27.61125	0	1	0	0	0	0	3383	16.9157	2761	13.8056
3	27.62125	1	1	0	0	0	0	3385	16.9257	2762	13.8106
4	27.63125	0	0	1	0	0	0	3387	16.9357	2763	13.8156
5	27.64125	1	0	1	0	0	0	3389	16.9457	2764	13.8206
6	27.65125	0	1	1	0	0	0	3391	16.9557	2765	13.8256
7	27.66125	1	1	1	0	0	0	3393	16.9657	2766	13.8306
8	27.67125	0	0	0	1	0	0	3395	16.9757	2767	13.8356
9	27.68125	1	0	0	1	0	0	3397	16.9857	2768	13.8406
10	27.69125	0	1	0	1	0	0	3399	16.9957	2769	13.8456
11	27.70125	1	1	0	1	0	0	3401	17.0057	2770	13.8506
12	27.71125	0	0	1	1	0	0	3403	17.0157	2771	13.8556
13	27.72125	1	0	1	1	0	0	3405	17.0257	2772	13.8606
14	27.73125	0	1	1	1	0	0	3407	17.0357	2773	13.8656
15	27.74125	1	1	1	1	0	0	3409	17.0457	2774	13.8706
16	27.75125	0	0	0	0	1	0	3411	17.0557	2775	13.8756
17	27.76125	1	0	0	0	1	0	3413	17.0657	2776	13.8806
18	27.77125	0	1	0	0	1	0	3415	17.0757	2777	13.8856

19	27.78125	0	1	1	0	0	1	3417	17.0857	2778	13.8906
20	27.79125	1	0	0	0	0	0	3419	17.0957	2779	13.8956
21	27.80125	1	0	0	0	0	1	3421	17.1057	2780	13.9006
22	27.81125	1	0	0	0	1	0	3423	17.1157	2781	13.9056
23	27.82125	1	0	0	1	1	1	3425	17.1257	2782	13.9106
24	27.83125	1	0	0	1	0	0	3427	17.1357	2783	13.9156
25	27.84125	1	0	0	1	0	1	3429	17.1457	2784	13.9206
26	27.85125	1	0	0	1	1	0	3431	17.1557	2785	13.9256
27	27.86125	1	0	0	0	1	1	3433	17.1657	2786	13.9306
28	27.87125	1	0	1	0	0	0	3435	17.1757	2787	13.9356
29	27.88125	1	0	1	0	0	1	3437	17.1857	2788	13.9406
30	27.89125	1	1	0	0	0	0	3439	17.1957	2789	13.9456
31	27.90125	1	1	0	0	0	1	3441	17.2057	2790	13.9506
32	27.91125	1	1	0	0	1	0	3443	17.2157	2791	13.9556
33	27.92125	1	1	0	1	1	1	3445	17.2257	2792	13.9606
34	27.93125	1	1	0	1	0	0	3447	17.2357	2793	13.9656
35	27.94125	1	1	0	1	0	1	3449	17.2457	2794	13.9706
36	27.95125	1	1	0	1	1	0	3451	17.2557	2795	13.9756
37	27.96125	1	1	0	0	1	1	3453	17.2657	2796	13.9806
38	27.97125	1	1	1	0	0	0	3455	17.2757	2797	13.9856
39	27.98125	1	1	1	0	0	1	3457	17.2857	2798	13.9906
40	27.99125	0	0	0	0	0	0	3459	17.2957	2799	13.9956

reference divider frequency) times 3451 (the receive divisor), which works out to 17.2550 MHz. You will see from Figure 11.1 that the v.c.o. output ranges from 16.9057 to 17.2957 MHz receive mode and from 13.8006 to 13.9957 MHz transmit mode, which is also shown in Table 11.3.

The frequency of the v.c.o. is reduced in the transmit mode by a factor of around 0.816 owing to the extra tuning capacitance switched in by Q2, as already noted. This causes the effective divisor to be less in the transmit than receive mode, as revealed in Table 11.3.

The transmit carrier frequency is obtained by doubling the v.c.o. output frequency. This is achieved by the doubler stage Q3, the transmit frequency then ranging from 27.60125 MHz (channel 1) to 27.99125 MHz (channel 40) over 10 kHz synthesized steps as selected by the channel switch. The precise channel frequency is obtained by adjusting the capacitance of the crystal reference oscillator by a small trimmer. This is not a user adjustment, of course, but is made under laboratory conditions for a frequency of 10.24046 MHz ±50 Hz.

In receive mode the synthesised frequency direct from the v.c.o. is used as the local oscillator signal for the receiver's first mixer.

The block labelled 'ch. 9' in Figure 11.1 refers to a switch on the front panel which when operated immediately applies the channel 9 code of 100100 for quickly accessing this distress or emergency channel, which is often monitored by enthusiastic CB groups.

Double superhet receive section

Figure 11.2 shows the block diagram of the transceiver as a whole. In receive mode the incoming signal from the CB aerial is applied to the emitter of a common base RF amplifier transistor Q7 via a coupling and matching transformer. The amplified signal from the collector is then fed to the first mixer which is a balanced circuit (helping with the rejection of unwanted spurious signals) consisting of a pair of bipolar

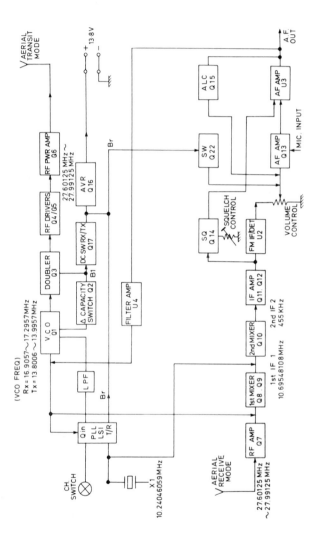

Figure 11.2. Block diagram of the Beta 3000 which is fully explained in the text

251

transistors Q8 and Q9. The coupling is by a bandpass transformer. The mixer also receives signal from the v.c.o. at a frequency related to the selected channel. When channel 36 is selected, for example, the aerial signal from a channel 36 transmission falls at 27.95125 MHz and the v.c.o. frequency is close to 17.255769 MHz. The difference between these two frequencies is 10.695481 MHz which is extremely close to the first intermediate-frequency (i.f.) shown on Figure 11.2.

This i.f. from the mixer is bandpass-coupled and filtered by a ceramic filter to provide good selectivity and then fed to the base of the second mixer Q10, which is a bipolar transistor arranged as a common emitter.

Now, an interesting point is that the local oscillator signal for the second mixer is obtained direct from the reference oscillator at (to be precise) 10.24046059 MHz. The difference between the first i.f. and the crystal reference frequency is 455 kHz which, of course, is the second i.f. This i.f. signal from the second mixer is again bandpass coupled and filtered by another (455 kHz one this time) ceramic filter and passed to a two-stage common-emitter i.f. amplifier, Q11 and Q12. The selectively is then very high, and exceptionally good 10 kHz channel separation is achieved.

Output of the i.f. amplifier is transformer-coupled to the f.m. detector, which is an IC quadrature detector U2. Audio from the detector is then passed to the common-emitter bipolar audio-frequency (a.f.) stage Q13 via the volume control and thence to the power amplifier IC U3, which drives the internal loudspeaker.

Transmission

Change from receive to transmit is activated by the press-to-talk (PTT) switch on the microphone. This biases-on switching transistor Q17 so that power is applied to the transmitter circuits. Transistor switch Q2 is also activated to reduce the v.c.o. frequency as already explained. After frequency-doubling by Q3, the r.f. signal is fed to an r.f. preamplifier which is a bipolar stage Q4. The signal then goes into an r.f. driver Q5 and thence to the r.f. power amplifier

Q6, where the signal is lifted to the legal maximum of 4 W into 50 ohms.

Tuned couplings are employed between the stages, the output-tuned circuit of the doubler selecting the 2nd-harmonic of the v.c.o. in transmit mode. The collector of the final power amplifier is tuned and the impedance is dropped to the required 50 ohms for coupling to the aerial socket by a form of L-pi network with additional low-pass filtering to ensure that harmonics of the carrier are adequately suppressed to the requirement of the Home Office, namely 50 nW in defined bands and 0.25 μW at any other frequency. An impedance-matching coupling is also used at the input of the final power amplifier transistor.

The carrier is frequency-modulated by the microphone signal, and in the transmit mode the a.f. amplifiers Q13 and IC U3 lift the audio to a suitable value, thus providing microphone gain. The Cybernet transceivers use a moving-coil or dynamic microphone. Amplified audio signal from the microphone is then fed to the filter amplifier U4 (Figure 11.2) and thence to another varicap diode located in the resonance circuit of the v.c.o. The capacitance of this diode thus changes in sympathy with the audio modulation, thereby frequency-modulating the carrier.

The filter amplifier provides a narrow-band audio characteristic by virtue of its two ICs and RC couplings. It cuts off audio frequencies above about 2.5 kHz sharply, thereby ensuring that the modulation bandwidth is retained within the limits prescribed for CB by the Home Office. A preset potentiometer at the input of the filter amplifier provides an adjustment of deviation.

Again, to keep within the Home Office requirement in terms of deviation, the automatic level control (ALC) stage Q15 holds the deviation at a constant value should the audio from the microphone become excessively high. The stage consists of a switching transistor and diode. The diode rectifies the audio signal and produces a negative voltage at its anode. When this exceeds a pre-determined level transistor Q15 switches on and bypasses the audio, thereby restoring the audio to the pre-determined level.

The transceiver is powered by a 12 V car battery or mains power supply delivering steady d.c. at a nominal 13.2 V (10.8 to 15.6 volts d.c., reversible ground) and consumes 1.5 A nominal in transmit mode and 1.2 A nominal in receive mode. The power input circuit includes an automatic voltage regulator (a.v.r.).

Four light-emitting diodes (l.e.d.s) indicate signal strength in receive mode and transmitter output in transmit mode, and the power can be reduced by 10 dB (necessary when the aerial is higher than 7 m) to around 400 mW by a rear switch, which reduces the output of the r.f. driver stage. The l.e.d.s also show the presence of modulation, particularly in the low-power setting.

On the *Beta 3000*, press-switches are present for selecting channel 9 (already mentioned), for dimming the digital channel display, for providing a PA function, thereby allowing the microphone to drive into an external speaker, and for modifying the response of the modulator channel by reducing the output at low frequencies. Sockets at the rear cater for the aerial (which switches automatically between transmit and receive), for an extension speaker and for a separate PA speaker.

In addition to the channel selector knob and volume control, this particular model includes an r.f. gain control (which adjusts the sensitivity of the r.f. amplifier), a tone control, which essentially reduces the treble output as it is turned anti-clockwise, and a squelch control which can be set to mute the audio output, thereby cutting out the noise, when the selected channel is free from signal. Depending on the setting of this control, the audio channel will open automatically when the channel is occupied by a CB signal of specific strength.

The above description is essentially common to the other Cybernet models which are the Beta 1000 and Beta 2000; also to many other CB rigs which are equipped with the Cybernet board. Cybernet transceivers are marketed and distributed in the UK by *Goodmans Loudspeakers Limited* of Havant.

The Cybernet Beta 3000 Professional is pictured in Figure 11.3. The Professional 3000 differs from the basic model in

Figure 11.3. The natty little Beta 3000 CB rig complete with Selcall

that it includes a small but sophisticated microcomputer which controls many of its operations, including a selective calling system (called Selcall) and control buttons on the microphone. The model is further equipped with auto-monitoring of channel 9 and auto-scanning for free or busy channels.

Selective calling

Selective calling is a scheme whereby the receiver section is allowed to continuously monitor incoming signals while being in the quiet, mute mode. On receipt of a specially-encoded call the mute is disabled and the call is detected. Various 'black boxes' providing selective calling have been evolved since the advent of legal CB to add to existing transceivers; but the advantage of the Professional 3000 is that the whole lot has been married within the rig's casing, so there's only the one unit to worry about.

With the Cybernet Selcall the receiver has a unique code which can be called by any other station of a group that is aware of it. When such a call is received, an acknowledgement tone is transmitted back to the caller. The station being called is made aware of the fact by his receiver producing a loud tone. Moreover, if the operator was away from his station at the time of the call he is informed on his return that he has been called because the letters CA and the channel number involved are caused to flash on and off when the call is transmitted.

The Selcall encoding is based on the hexadecimal notation to increase the possible combinations. There are 4048 numbers per channel which are divided into 16 banks of 256 call codes per channel, so the possibility of other users having the same call codes is not very high. Coding can be internally preset as required. Time of code transmission is around 1 second, and the system operates independently of the rig's squelch control, access level being automatic.

The licencing conditions allow for the use of selective calling signals or digital transmissions designed solely to identify the transmitter. Apart from this the stipulation is for plain speech only, as already noted.

Selective calling systems can enhance the use of CB radio for the more 'business' type of applications in terms of a fairly reliable, low-cost method of communication between mobiles, base station to mobile or base to base. It represents another way of putting CB radio to work.

934 MHz CB

At the time of writing, there are relatively few 934 MHz CB stations operating. Tests and research conducted by the author have indicated that 934 MHz CB is more affected by weather conditions than 27 MHz CB and that local screening and topography can influence it much more than 27 MHz.

Feeder losses at the higher frequency are also that much greater, and from the permitted 8 W of r.f. and 4-element Yagi aerials it would so far appear that the Home Office was somewhat optimistic in refering to 25 W maximum e.r.p. Deterioration of the conductor surfaces of aerials and the connections to the feeder would appear to diminish the radiating efficiency with time unless special heed is taken in the design at the frequency involved of possible u.h.f. skin effects.

At the time of writing there were indications of the development of transverters for connecting to 27 MHz rigs, thereby allowing their use also on 934 MHz, but possible problems here have not yet been exposed by protracted field use.

As already noted, the use of 934 MHz equipment has not yet (at the time of writing!) really taken off, and it is, presumably, before this does happen that the Home Office (Radio Regulatory Department) wants to get the 934 MHz CB channels realigned to the CEPT plan. There are, nevertheless, 934 MHz rigs in operation so with the advent of the realignment, problems will be posed for manufacturers, dealers and users. It will probably be feasible to retune some models to cater for the −12.5 kHz per channel offset; but others could call for crystal changes as well.

Another problem will be that transceivers based on the original frequencies will not be wholly compatible with transceivers using the CEPT-plan frequencies. Although the 12.5 kHz offset will still fall in the receiver's i.f. passband the slight detuning between transceivers of the new and old standards could well be detected in fringe reception areas, as also the increased distortion arising from the lack of optimisation of the receiver to the signals. It would appear just as well, therefore, that there are not many 934 MHz CB rigs yet in the field!

From the design point of view, the problems are more severe at 934 MHz than at 27 MHz, avoidance of frequency drift with temperature change (despite crystal-controlled frequency synthesisation) and microphony being but two of them; but happily they are being resolved, although it seems likely that the 934 MHz models will remain that much higher in price than their 27 MHz counterparts.

Minimising interference

It is the duty of CB users to ensure that their equipment does not cause undue inteference to other services, it being a condition of the licence for the equipment to be so designed, constructed and maintained. CB interference might well be experienced, for example, on some TV receivers when the CB aerial is sited close to and in front of the TV aerial. The best plan in this case would be to re-site the CB aerial for maximum spacing behind the TV aerial (the reflector side).

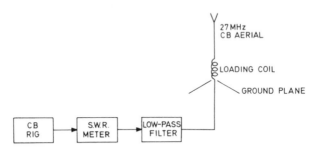

Figure 11.4. The inclusion of a low-pass filter between the 27 MHz CB aerial and the CB rig or s.w.r. meter ensures that the transmitter output is free from strong harmonics and high-frequency spuriae

Filtering can also help at the TV receiver itself, as noted in Chapter 3. To ensure a 'clean' signal from the CB rig it is undesirable to keep in circuit certain types of s.w.r. meters and aerial preamplifiers, since the diodes in these can sometimes introduce strong harmonics of the transmitter's carrier frequency. To make sure that the CB output signal is free from upper-frequency spuriae and harmonics, the use of a low-pass filter between the aerial socket of the CB set and the aerial feeder is to be recommended. If an s.w.r. meter is installed permanently in circuit, then the filter should be located after this, as shown in Figure 11.4. The same applies if an aerial preamplifier is used to boost the incoming signal. The filter should, in general, always be placed between the aerial and any other equipment; though with some amateur radio transmitters, which incorporate a separate aerial tuning unit (a.t.u.), the filter may be best located after this – between it and an s.w.r. meter, for example.

As its name implies, a low-pass filter lets through the frequencies from the transmitter while attenuating higher-frequency signals, such as spuriae and harmonics as shown by the characteristic at (a) in Figure 11.5. The actual attenuation, of course, must occur at a higher frequency than the transmission frequency, so the filter's turnover point must be chosen to suit the frequency involved. Basic circuit of a low-pass filter is given at (b) in Figure 11.5 while, to complete the picture, the circuit of a high-pass filter which might be used in the aerial circuit of an affected TV receiver is shown at (c) and its characteristic at (d); but also see Chapter 3.

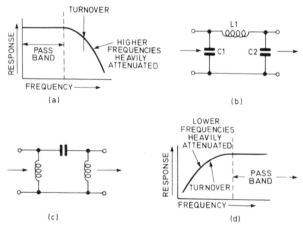

Figure 11.5. (a) response characteristics of a low-pass filter. (b) circuit of simple, single-stage low-pass filter. (c) circuit of simple, single-stage, high-pass filter. (d) response characteristics of a high-pass filter. Also see Chapter 3

As already noted, legal 27 MHz CB aerials are equipped with a base-loading inductor and this itself affords some attenuation to harmonics from the transmitter, thereby reducing the risk of interference to certain classes of receiving equipment.

Index